L³

Lean Operations, Lean Design, Lean Construction

Building a Lean Hospital Facility

Akron Children's Hospital

COMPILED BY THE AKRON CHILDREN'S TOWER TEAM

L³: Building a Lean Hospital Facility

Editor, project manager and writing coach: Tonya Vinas

Designer: Megan Lasalla, MHL Designs

Printed by: Signature Book Printing, www.sbpbooks.com

ISBN: 978-0-578-14848-9

Table of **Contents**

 Building a Lean Hospital Facility

Welcome

One of my favorite movie scenes is the Circle of Life from Disney's 1994 The Lion King. The song lyrics and beautiful imagery remind me of what we strive for at Akron Children's Hospital: family-centered care, strength of community, and the joy of life that every child embodies.

With the Kay Jewelers Pavilion project, our hospital gains not only a new building, but also the privilege of participating in a new part of the Circle of Life. One result of using Integrated Project Delivery to design and build the Tower was a freeing up of enough resources to add high-risk delivery service, so that babies that

need immediate care receive it when they need — immediately.

In 2008 our hospital embraced Operations Excellence as a foundational strategy and began using the principles of lean management and Six Sigma to improve our work and make strategic decisions based on what is best according to the needs of patients, patient families and the communities we serve.

In some ways we had to radically change our thinking, working and planning. In other ways, Operations Excellence easily aligned with our history and culture Children and their healthcare needs

To Our Journey

have always been our mission, even as healthcare itself undergoes dramatic change.

Today, we remain focused on the needs of any child that walks through our doors, regardless of their family's ability to pay. Our goal is to make every child's life as joyful as it can be through family-centered care, community support and exceptional clinical experiences. We strive to treat all children as if they were our own and design our services and facilities through their eyes.

Welcome to the story of our Kay Jewelers Pavilion journey and our ongoing commitment to the Circle of Life.

Sincerely,

William H. Considine

William Considine
President and CEO,
Akron Children's Hospital

History *of* Akron Children's Hospital

1930: Growing With The Community

The nursery grew to a 100-bed hospital in 1930 to meet the needs of the growing community and to support the rubber industry. The organization continued to thrive through the war and the polio epidemic.

1890

1930

1970

1890: Dedicated To Children's Care

A group of dedicated women decided to provide child care for the families of Akron's factory workers in the home of Col. George Tod Perkins. From this, the Mary Day Nursery grew to include caring for sick children.

1970: Firsts For Sick Infants And Burned Children

By 1970, Akron Children's Hospital had added one of the region's first Neonatal Intensive Care Units and a Regional Burn Center.

Akron Children's Hospital Today*

Owned or leased beds	390
Employees	4,751
Medical staff	703
Volunteers	1,360
Patient days	70,418
Emergency visits	95,676
Surgeries	14,892
Outpatient visits	683,537
School-health visits	373,988
Home-care visits	4,272
Gross Revenue	$1,063,495,000
% Medicaid	49.4%
Community benefit (2012)	$107,300,000

*12/31/14 statistics

Early 1990s: Focus Moves To Family-Centered Care

The hospital's thriving mission of providing family-centered care, education, research, community service and advocacy prompted the addition of a new building in 1993, the Centennial Building. This latest addition promoted the delivery of family-centered care by offering private accommodations with rooming-in for parents. Gone were the days that parents dropped their children off at the hospital or were considered visitors.

Early 2000s

Akron Children's grew with the addition of the Considine Professional building, an addition to provide private-room Pediatric Intensive Care Unit beds, a larger Burn Center and private hematology oncology rooms.

early 1990

mid 1990

early 2000s

post 2010

Mid-1990s: Independent, With A Growing Network

Healthcare reform prompted a wave of hospital mergers and acquisitions, but Akron Children's Board of Directors wanted to remain independent, serving all children of the region, regardless of their ability to pay. The Board and President Bill Considine determined the hospital had to develop an integrated pediatric health care system with a regional presence and a strong primary care network. Akron Children's Hospital Physicians network was born.

This network, which has grown to 25 primary care offices in northern Ohio, positioned the hospital to transition to a population-based delivery system that today includes a home-care entity, school-health service, a professional-liability company, a foundation and a population health-management company.

Post-2010

By 2011, the hospital needed additional space for physician practices, operating rooms, emergency department services and neonatal intensive care beds. The hospital did not have an independent outpatient surgery center and required all simple outpatient cases to be co-mingled and delayed by inpatient and urgent cases. Hospital leadership and the Board decided an updated Master Planning initiative for the campus was in order. The Tower is an outcome of that plan, Master Plan 2030.

Prologue:

Integrated Project Delivery

Source: Scott Nolin, Principal Consultant for KLMK Group

Integrated Project Delivery (IPD) is the design-build project delivery method that Akron Children's Hospital chose to use in the Tower project.

There are several design-build project delivery methods. Three common ones include:

- Design-Bid-Build (Hard Bid Method)
- Design Build
- Construction Management at Risk (vs. Agency CM)

IPD is a relatively new delivery model. The main concept behind IPD is to improve team collaboration through structured risk-and-reward management and sharing in an attempt to form a more streamlined, functional and successful project team (and hence project) for the benefit of all involved parties

In IPD the Owner goes through a selection process to integrate the design and construction team early in the process. This can extend to design sub-consultants and key sub-contractors. The selected project team then enters into an Integrated Form of Agreement (IFOA) with the Owner thereby creating a three-party contractual relationship among the owner, architect and the contractor.

One of the biggest differences of an IPD project versus a traditional construction project is that many more people influence design. In these photos, a cross-section of hospital employees participate in design planning at a warehouse where mocked-up replicas of patient rooms, surgery rooms, treatment rooms, intensive-care units, reception areas and other spaces were used for testing scenarios.

Some of the things that are different in an IPD project compared with traditional methods are the contract, insurance, fees, incentives, tools and processes, estimating, information sharing, risk sharing, group management, early integration of teams and a focus on end cost not bid day.

The critical keys to success for an IPD project are:

- Trust and commitment to the approach

- Decisive and involved owner

- Effective team selection process and the right team

- Effective project charter/owner's program

- Equitable contract that manages and balances risk and reward for the entire team

- Integrated approach to problem solving

- Constant focus on the end result and the big picture

Building Your Knowledge

IPD Resources

Integrated Project Delivery For Public and Private Owners, The Associated General Contractors of America, **www.agc.org**

Integrated Project Delivery: A Guide, The American Institute of Architects, **www.aia.org**

IPD Case Studies, The American Institute of Architects, **www.aia.org**

IPD Teams

Akron Children's Hospital – Owner
Grace Wakulchik, COO

Mike Trainer, CFO

Lin Gentile, VP of Construction & Support Services

Cliff Greive, Director of Construction

Sheryl Valentine, Lean Six Sigma Deployment Leader/Center for Operations Excellence

David Chand, M.D., Lean Six Sigma Deployment Director/Center for Operations Excellence

Trauda Gilbert, Lean Six Sigma Deployment Leader/Center for Operations Excellence

Tim Ziga, Associate General Counsel

Doug Dulin, Administrative Director/Center for Operations Excellence*

CBRE — Owner Representatives
Ray Walker, Managing Director

Stephen Powell, Consultant

Magnus Nilsson, Senior Consultant*

Scott Nolin, Principal Consultant with KLMK Group*

CONSTRUCTION

The Boldt Company
Dave Kievet, Group President

Will Lichtig, Vice President, Business and Process Development

Trent Jezwinski, Director

Nick Loughrin, Project Manager

Welty Building Company
Don Taylor, President and CEO

Patrick Oaks, Project Executive

Paul Becks, Project Field Manager

ARCHITECTURE

HKS – Dallas
Jeff Stouffer, AIA, Principal, Pediatric Healthcare Practice Leader

John Bienko, AIA, Principal, Project Manager

Bernita Beikmann, AIA, Principal, Director of Lean Strategy

Rachel Knox, AIA, Associate Principal, Pediatric Healthcare Leader

Norio Tsuchiya, AIA, Vice President

Ramon Cavazos, AIA, Associate

Jennie Evans, RN, BSN – Associate Principal, Sr. Vice President

Mike Mamer, AIA, Vice President

Hasenstab Architects
Bob Medziuch, Principal

Marge Zezulewicz, AIA

Scott Radcliff, AIA

Mark Ohlinger, Principal, Retired*

MEP/F Engineers
CCRD
Rick Rome, President/CEO

Sarah Kuchera, Associate Principal

John Skinner, Senior Associate

Bandwen Williams Kindbom
Tom Bandwen, President

Kevin Kindbom, Vice President

Thorson Baker – Structural Engineers
Mike Thorson, Principle

Cole Hamey, Project Engineer

Mitchell Planning Associates – Medical Planners
Lisa Charrin, Vice President

Jennifer Lieb, Project Manager

Environmental Design Group – Civil Landscape and Design
Dwayne Groll, PE, LEED-AP, President

Travis Matthews, Sr. Group Leader

Jill Ward, LEED AP, Project Engineer

Gerard Neugebauer, P.E., LEED AP, Project Manager

Dynamix Engineering – Technology Engineering
Garry Montgomery, Vice President

Craig Buchholz, Engineering Manager

Senior Leadership Team
Grace Wakulchik, Owner/COO

Jeff Stouffer, AIA, HKS/Principal, Pediatric Healthcare Practice Leader

Bob Medziuch, AIA, Hasenstab Architects/ Principal

Dave Kievet, The Boldt Company/ Group President

Don Taylor, The Welty Building Company/ President and COE

Project Leadership Team
Lin Gentile, Owner/VP for Construction and Support Services

Cliff Greive, Owner/Director of Construction

John Bienko, AIA, HKS, Principal, Project Manager

Marge Zezulewicz, AIA, Hasenstab Architects

Pat Oaks, Welty Building Company/ Project Executive

Ray Walker, CBRE/Project Director

Trent Jezwinski, The Boldt Company/Director

*Participated in limited segments

17

Project Timeline

2012

June 6

Groundbreaking on new parking garage

August 29

Town hall meeting where parents (and kids) give input on design

December 10-14

Identifying best practices (teams meet to discuss and collaborate on creating the most value in design)

August 12

Announcement of $200 million expansion project

September 10-14

Outpatient Surgery Center warehouse design meeting

September 25

Second town hall meeting with parents

November 13

Third town hall for NICU "graduates"

August 13-17

First warehouse design meeting (ER) focusing on size

October 14-19

NICU warehouse design meeting

BUILDING a Lean Hospital Facility

Akron Children's Hospital

2013   2014

January 21
Fourth town hall meeting for parents' input on design

Department process work and A3 development
Equipment selection

February 4-8
Final NICU design workshop at warehouse

Spring 2015
COMPLETION

May 20
Ceremonial groundbreaking, construction begins

May 10
First high-risk delivery paves way for new service

How to Use this Book

*By Sheryl Valentine, Lean Six Sigma Deployment Leader/
Center for Operations Excellence, Akron Children's Hospital*

We hope you find this book helpful as you consider Lean Project Design for your next capital project. If lean is new to your organization or you would simply like to learn more or dig deeper, we have added some helpful sections in each chapter that will guide your efforts.

Project Name

The official name of our new building is the Kay Jewelers Pavilion, but throughout the book we refer to it as the Tower, which was our working name before the official christening.

Graphs and Tables

The graphs, drawings and maps helping to hone the points in each chapter are from our actual design and process work.

Tips From The Trenches

As we moved through our Integrated Project Delivery (IPD) process, we continued to learn. Tips From the Trenches are our "lessons learned" that we would like to pass on as you embark on this journey.

Building Your Knowledge

Some of the subject matter in this book may be new, or maybe you would like to learn more about a particular topic. Several of the chapters have bibliographies or references for further reading. These were references we used to develop our education programs, kept on hand as we worked in the design and construction phase, and continue to use as we develop our process work preparing for occupancy in our new space.

E³: Engagement, Everyone, Everywhere

Furthering the lean principle of honoring people through process participation, we looked for and acted upon opportunities to include "unofficial" IPD project team members. These stories are told in E3 breakout boxes.

Finally, as of the completion of this edition, the Kay Jewelers Pavilion was still under construction (ahead of schedule) as we planned our transition and occupancy. Stay tuned for future updates from the trenches!

Introduction

Family-Centered Care Through Operational Excellence

By Grace Wakulchik, COO, VP of Operations,
RN, MSN, MBA, Akron Children's Hospital

Akron Children's Hospital's mission, vision and promises remain true to the culture our founders established on the basis of three promises:

- Treat every child as we would our own;

- Treat everyone the way we'd want to be treated; and,

- Never turn a child away.

These promises promote service above self; respect for all patients, families and co-workers; passion for the mission; commitment to the community; collaboration; genuine kindness; and the pursuit of excellence and continuous improvement to better the lives of children. We believe in family-centered care and that dignity, information sharing, respect, involvement and collaboration should be applied not only to the families we serve, but also to the families of the members of our organization and our community.

See next page: 2014-2016 Strategic Plan

Akron Children's Hospital
2014–2016 Strategic Plan

Akron Children's Hospital

True North Objectives

Quality & Care Transformation

Patient Experience

Market Position

Education & Discovery

Operational Imperatives

People

Technology & Analytics

Facilities

Financial Health

Vision

Promises

Mission

Culture

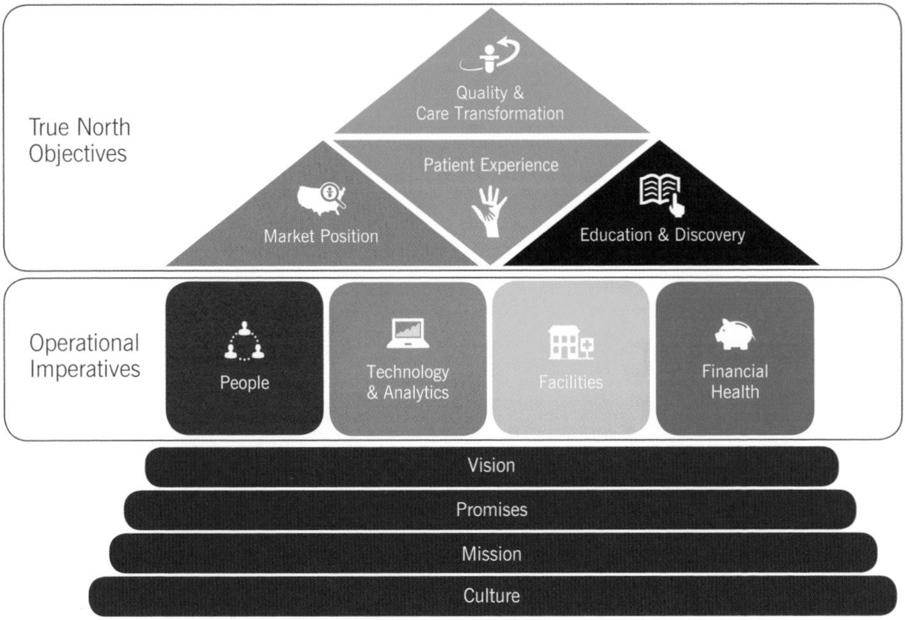

Mission Statement

Akron Children's Hospital is dedicated to *improving* the health of *children* through *outstanding* quality patient care, education, advocacy, *community* service, and *discovery.*

Center For Operations Excellence

The spirit of lean management became part of our culture in 2008. In the past, we had invested significantly in consultants to improve clinical quality and operational effectiveness, but the expertise to continue that journey usually walked out the door when they did.

Mark Watson, COO at the time, took on a challenge posed by the CEO to develop a comprehensive program that would develop internal expertise and a culture that embraced continuous improvement.

Mark identified six team members with the credibility and leadership potential to advance this strategy: a physician, a pharmacist, a nurse, two managers and a data analyst. He then selected an administrative assistant and hired an external lean consultant and Master Black Belt, who eventually became the first director of our Center for Operations Excellence (COE). The six individuals were titled deployment directors and began studying lean management and Six Sigma. All became Black Belts over the next few years.

Recognition And Affiliations

Over the past 20 years, Akron Children's has transitioned from what was known as the best kept secret in pediatric healthcare to the 10th largest pediatric system in the United States (2013 AHA Guide). The small, one-building hospital became the region's largest provider of care to children with two hospital campus locations (Akron and Youngstown), eight pediatric or neonatal units embedded in regional hospitals, four emergency departments, 25 primary care offices, affiliations with two major providers in the Cleveland area, and many subspecialty offices.

Recognition and awards include:

- **Magnet Recognition Program:** Recognizes healthcare organizations for quality patient care, nursing excellence and innovations in professional nursing practice.

- *US News and World Report* **award for Best Children's Hospital:** An annual ranking by 150 pediatric specialists as to where they would send their sickest children.

- **NorthCoast 99 Award:** An annual recognition of the top 99 workplaces in Northeast Ohio.

- **Most Wired Award:** Benchmark for level of IT adoption in the United States.

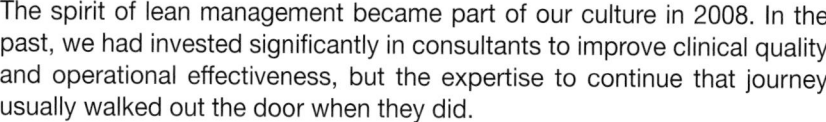

Master Plan 2030

Master Plan 2030: Early project rendering.

Our Akron campus expansion and collaboration with regional partners led to success in physician and provider recruitment. By 2010, Akron Children's had more than 700 medical staff members, more than 400 of which were employed. Even with the expansion into the region to support the delivery of care "close to home," we lacked sufficient capacity for clinic space, operating rooms, and critical care beds.

Space for new programs — such as expanded sleep labs, a wellness center, interventional radiology, inpatient rehab services, an obesity program, an expanded GI program, a sports medicine center, sedation services, infusion centers and a dental program — were nonexistent. To address space and over-crowded conditions, we relocated outpatient behavioral health services, allergy services and other administrative functions in leased space near the campus. In addition, lack of parking was the favorite topic of discontent with families and staff.

We needed a new vision for the Akron campus in 2010 which was a good problem to have at the time. Akron Children's had been improving its financial position for several years, and commercial as well as residential construction had slowed to a crawl as a result of the 2008 recession. We hired Karlsberger Healthcare Consulting to develop a master plan to carry the Akron campus through the next 50 years.

Karlsberger delivered a seven-stage master plan that included two parking structures, a critical care tower, an ambulatory care building, a diagnostic and therapeutic center and a specialty hospital. The plan phased the new buildings in over the following 20 years and phased out the 100-year-old parts of the building, identified largely by the occupants as the area where they lost cell phone coverage. The plan was presented to and approved by the Board of Directors on Sept. 27, 2012.

Master Plan 2030	Key Elements
Phase 1	1,000-space parking structure, medical office building, lobby atrium, critical care tower (NICU PICU, Burn Center), helipad
Phase 2	Diagnostic-and-treatment center: OR, Sterile Processing, Materials Management, Imaging, Lab
Phase 3	Specialty Services, 600-space parking structure
Phase 4	Energy plant
Phase 5	Research building
Phase 6	Medical office building
Phase 7	Ronald McDonald House

Property Acquisition

TIPS From the Trenches:
Plan Ahead, Seek Expertise, Allow For Demolition Requirements

- Develop a property-management plan designating which properties on or off the major campuses will be owned or leased.

- Acquire property surrounding the campus and strategic locations as part of a regular buying program to ensure best prices and avoid time delays in project deployment.

- Retain top talent in real estate management through acquisition or contracting to ensure best practices. Most hospitals don't have this talent internally. You wouldn't expect your real estate agent to take your daughter's tonsils out. Stick to the business of running a healthcare organization.

- When demolishing old buildings on property that have been on inhabited grounds with vintage sewer and utility lines, include time and expense for asbestos abatement, utility relocations, historical processes, locations of time capsules and donations to charitable re-use organizations.

Fortunately, the hospital had land-banked numerous properties over the years and had an excellent relationship with city officials. However, we had to acquire additional properties. The surrounding businesses had no compelling reason to relocate, particularly because owners believed their property was undervalued due to the downturn in the real estate market. The negotiation and sale of these properties took considerable time and patience because they were valued community partners, and the intent was to "keep them whole," which meant paying for relocation expenses and facility upgrades.

The design and location of Phase 1 was fluid as the possibilities of acquiring necessary properties fluctuated. A basic pull plan with the key date of breaking ground in May 2013 set an aggressive schedule to negotiate agreements, and provide for relocation time and demolition.

A new key hire in our Legal Department, Tim Ziga, enabled the successful completion of our real estate transactions.

Phase 1: Discovery and Planning

The first phase of the Master Plan was to build a new parking deck to accommodate displaced parkers from the future construction site, build a critical care tower and a new ambulatory care building. We hired a consultant to do some preliminary planning regarding the potential square-footage requirements in light of the relocation of programs in leased space, program growth and the space required for new programs.

Blue Cottage Consulting provided a charette. Krentz Consulting provided data based on market share, local and regional growth, competitors and changes in healthcare utilization trends. A rough estimate of 300,000 square feet at $600 per square foot led us to an estimate of $180 million for the buildings.

A parking study identified our future need for parking to be around 1,100 spaces, and $20 million was targeted for the new parking deck.

After much discussion, we decided to engage an owner's representative. Internal staff had hoped to manage the project without additional representation, but at the encouragement of the CEO and the Board of Directors, we selected KLMK (now CBRE) as the owner's representative. We had sent a survey to the COOs of other children's hospitals to identify qualified owner's representatives, and the responses reinforced that we needed someone who would get up every day and only worry about the project.

Looking back, we see that our culture of respect for staff, kindness, continuous improvement and collaboration led us down the right path.

TIPS From The Trenches
Think Big on Resources Needed

- Don't manage a sizable project without an owner's representative — contracted or employed. Your staff needs to operate a hospital. They can't put that on hold for four years. Major construction is not an "add on" project.

- Take time and due diligence to select an owner's representative that understands your mission (in our case pediatric hospitals), your vision and your culture.

- Always analyze and address parking needs. Do a formal parking study. If your staff and patients can't get to you, it doesn't matter how excellent your buildings and providers are. Interim parking plans during construction are critical for patient and staff satisfaction, maintenance of market share and safety.

Tapping Into Our Lean Sub-Culture

The lean sub-culture developing at Akron Children's became the driving force in the establishment of the building program. Absent the successes of the work of our COE, this project would have followed a course of a traditional building project. As one of the deployment directors of the COE noted, the building project also cemented the principles, tools and systems of lean into the hospital's existing culture.

The project transformation started where most successful change does: in the minds and hands of the front-line staff who do the most valued work. The tag line for the COE is "Process improvement through people development." It was our people who made this project distinctive and successful.

Lean Tools: We recognized that our culture, mission and promises already aligned with lean principles, but as an organization, we lacked knowledge about tools, so that's where we started.

We began with classes on A3 thinking and improvement projects. To date more than 400 staff members have learned about and completed an A3 project. Green Belt training then began, and we encouraged high-potential team members to become Green Belts to further embed the culture of continuous improvement. Today more than 11 staff members are Green Belts.

Finally, the highest-profile tool that was initiated in the early years was the kaizen rapid-improvement process. While the COE had quietly begun to promote change and operational improvement in departments that volunteered to participate, introducing kaizens raised awareness throughout the organization of what could be done with this new method.

In one example, we avoided spending more than $3 million in improvements to Sterile Processing while improving performance. This was real money. Improving scheduling in Radiology to add $1.3 million for MRI imaging that was going elsewhere due to scheduling challenges? Real money and, more importantly, patient satisfaction!

Lean Principles: As the lean sub-culture continued to develop, it became apparent that the front-line staff were gaining improvement skills that couldn't be supported at the manager level, so the COE established a plan for leader and manager education. Leaders attended classes at ThedaCare in Appleton, Wis., a pioneering lean healthcare organization. The CEO, COO, CFO, Vice President for Human Resources, Executive Vice President and other key executive staff members attended. Lean education, rounding in the workplace, huddles, lean finance and A3 thinking learned at ThedaCare prepared our leaders to support our new lean experts.

Strategic Goal Deployment Matrix

EXECUTIVE LEADERSHIP — TIER 5 and 6 X MATRIX — STRATEGY DE

Correlation

EpicCare Link or EPIC access (Read-Only)
Complete Building Program per schedule
Implement and Expand GI/Digestive Disease Center
Evaluate and Implement Interventional Radiology Program
Plan for the implementation of High Risk OB Services
Develop Plan for multidisciplinary ambulatory sites (Mansfield, Medina, Northern Tier, Trumbull)
Partner with Community Hospitals for Inpatient Services (Wooster, St. Joes)
Expand ACHP with 3 new sites (Northern tier, MV, Trumbull)
Evaluate Heart Center Partnership with CCF
Finalize plan for new ambulatory Services Building and/or backfill plan
Improve Financial Performance
Continue EPIC ambulatory rollout and upgrade to EPIC 2012
Implement ICD-10
Meet meaningful use Stage II for EH and EP for Stage I
Expand MyChart Rollout
Implement Systems and processes to enhance/ promote workforce development
Recruit and Retain top Talent/ Focus on retention
Develop plan for employee wellness center
Develop clinical plan that aligns clinical care/ service delivery w/ bus. model pursued in risk-based contracting
Raise $10M for the Promise campaign
Complete Community Assessment and action plan for Akron and MV
Support and enhance the medical/surgical research portfolio
Develop plan and recommendations regarding fellowship and Resident Training
Plan for integrated Telehealth Program & Video communications
Reduce Patient Harm
Develop global patient services & relationships (Out of region & International)
Develop/expand patient experience initiatives and tools

Key Initiatives

Transformational Improvements 2014

(logo) Akron Children's Hospital

Target Metric: 50, 75%, 3, 850, 400, 50, 1, 2, 26

Baseline: 0, 25%, 0, 240, 0, 0, 0, 0, 23

Key Metrics

# of providers connected via EpicCare Link
% of construction complete
# of GI Providers hired
# of GI Visits
# IR Providers hired
# of IR Procedures
% of HROB Operational Plan Completed
# of Multidisciplinary Sites opened
# of new Inpatient units opened
# of ACHP opened

3 - 5 Year True North Objectives

People — Become Northern Ohio's Healthcare Employer of Choice
Quality/Pat Exp/Care Transformation — Become the pre-eminent, highest value pediatric healthcare provider in OH; become pediatric healthcare organization of choice in Northern OH by transforming the delivery of care
Financial Stability — Maintain independent status and stability while achieving Aa3 bond rating
Market Position — Become #1 (market share) provider of pediatric healthcare in northern OH
Academics: Research and Education — Develop the identity and scope of research and academics in the organization

Align non-employed community providers
Prepare for Population Health Management
Develop a strategic plan for Academics and Research
Expand Clinical services to meet community and patient needs
Design, Build and Maintain infrastructure to support services
Align Community Service and Advocacy with Community need
Expand Evidence-Based Practice
Refine Culture of Patient Safety
Enhance culture of Philanthropy
Achieve operating margin of 4%
Optimize employee and physician performance
Enhance Patient Experience

Correlation

Date: 9/18/2014 | Reporting Unit: Executive Leadership

Additionally, the COE created a Blue Belt program to provide managers and directors at the organization — in collaboration with the vice presidents and leaders of the medical staff — education on Akron Children's Lean Operating System. The curriculum included the development of leader standard work, the use of lean tools, the development of key operational and quality metrics, the quality cross and daily huddles. To date, more than 93% of the organization's managers are huddling.

Lean Design and Construction: In 2011, the leaders of the areas involved in the new building project attended a two-day presentation on lean hospital design by Joan Wellman of Joan Wellman and Associates. This was a transformational moment for the project. The presentation changed the mindset of those in attendance about the approach that should be taken for the new building. No longer could we conceive of building a structure that was not driven by lean principles.

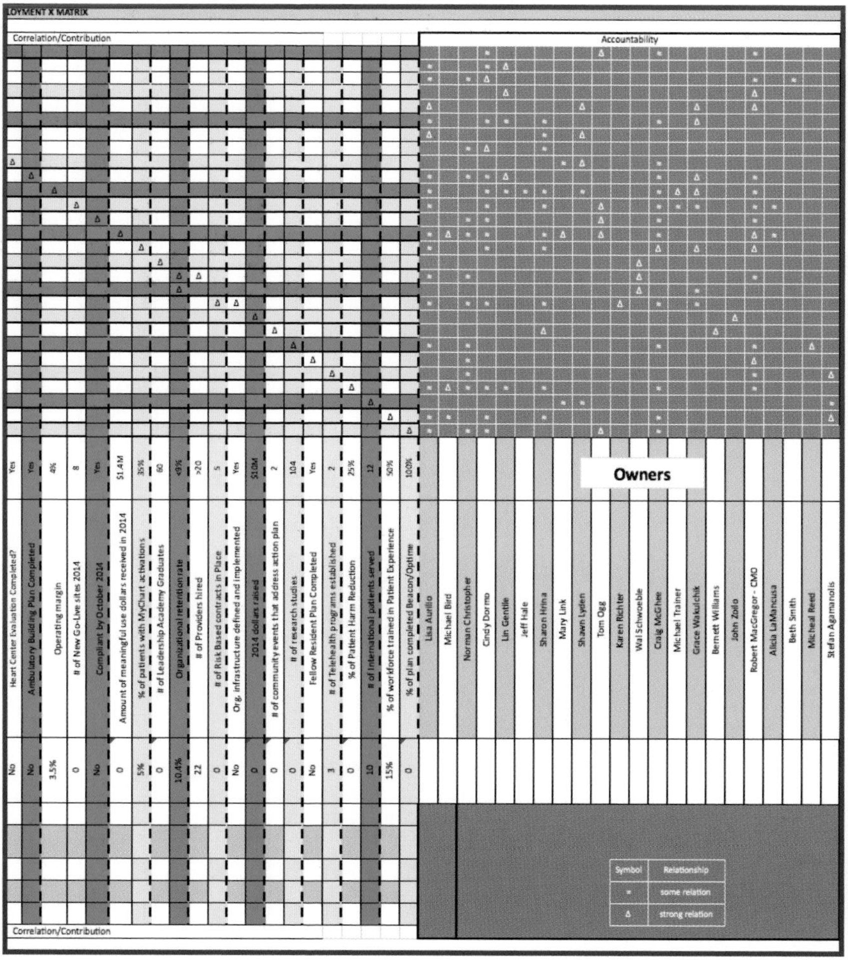

DEPLOYMENT X MATRIX

Correlation/Contribution — Accountability

Owners

Symbol	Relationship
□	some relation
△	strong relation

Joan noted that the process she promoted was not Integrated Project Delivery (IPD), but Integrated Facility Design. Why would we design a building that was not first and foremost to meet the needs of our patients and families and the optimal-care delivery model? Why would we design a building and then force operations to work in that footprint? Shouldn't design support process?

Our team was on fire. We weren't going to build waste, and we had always done what was right for patients and families. This was our culture.

Lean Systems: By 2011, the organization had embraced lean and identified that the important resources of the COE should be used to support the hospital's strategic direction and initiatives. If the COE was not perceived to be providing value to these important goals, its continued existence could be at risk. The value of the COE could be questioned. Would we need this resource if we had created this expertise among the staff and leaders? We took the opportunity to implement hoshin kanri, or strategic goal deployment using an x-matrix to display the organization's strategic priorities, annual transformational goals, key initiatives, success metrics and accountability. We use Huddle boards to track metrics and performance at different levels, called Tiers, at the executive level.

Developing the x-matrix was challenging for executives and board members who had never seen this sort of document. It is big. It is confusing. There are numbers everywhere. You have to turn it to read it.

But it is all on one page, and it is important. It reflects our strategic and annual direction. It helps us (but doesn't prevent us!) from running after those bright, shiny objects that have the propensity to deter us from our established course. It focuses our efforts on those goals that the organization has deemed are critical for us to accomplish. The metrics from the x-matrix are on the huddle boards.

Strategic Goal Deployment: Tier 5 strategy deployment x-matrix.

Information Flows: A Tier 3 Huddle board.

All huddles roll up through departments and divisions to the executive huddle (Tier 5), which takes place every day at noon in my office.

This method has enhanced communications, improved key safety and other metrics issues and made interdisciplinary opportunities for improvement more visible. We talk about medication errors, unplanned extubations, employee falls, parking bus schedules, construction updates, flu vaccination rates, volumes, IT issues, and more — every day. Information flows back to the Tier 1-4 huddles. Rumors get squashed and teamwork is enhanced.

L³: Lean Operations, Lean Design, Lean Construction

While evaluating the application of lean to our construction project, we wanted more than just lean operations, lean design and lean construction. We wanted to tap into our culture and expand our learning and capabilities. We saw this potential in the IPD methodology. IPD methodology provided a collaborative, proactive team approach to apply our lean work.

We were interested in collaboration, bringing a team together early to learn from the best we had to offer to provide value to the project, one contract for all, one contingency pool, and one incentive pool. We liked the idea of not suing each other. We liked the idea that we would work together to deliver the best value to our patients and families and not waste a dime. That was our culture. We wanted to find partners to join us on that journey.

Lean operations were key to our project. Our teams gathered information about other similar projects and began to understand that if Operations drove design, there would be greater value for the patients and less waste (costly rework).

Understanding operations meant involving our patients and families, as well as staff. We brought them in on Day 1. They participated in the value stream mapping of current and future operations as well as the design process described in later chapters. The clinical users and the families were our secret sauce. They provided a north star for the project. Our lean experts ensured that our lean design was data driven, so value was front and center. We weren't building trauma space to manage all the patients from that school bus accident we had 20 years ago. We would build the rooms we needed based on data and develop contingency plans to handle outliers.

Lean design might have been our starting point, but it was one part of many within the lean program for the project. It certainly had considerable visibility as we brought our user teams of clinicians, families, architects and construction staff to the Big Room to design on paper and then in full scale cardboard mock ups in a warehouse. It looked like fun, and it was, but there was a tremendous amount of work done to set up clinical scenarios for simulation, analysis of travel times, clinician workflow patterns and family use of space.

A class in session where planning and testing of mocked-up designs took place.

INTEGRATED LEAN PROJECT DELIVERY®

Although the process we used is generally known as Integrated Project Delivery, officially, we called our methodology Integrated Lean Project Delivery (ILPD®), trademarked by the BOLDT company. The process enabled us to use lean methodology in our contracting method and an Owner Controlled Insurance Program (OCIP) (both described in the Appendix) to reduce insurance costs and provide value in improved coverage.

Finally, we used lean construction to turn this hard work into a concrete outcome. We heard stories of 50% waste in construction. We hate waste. We wanted to identify a construction partner that would bring lean construction, prefabrication, building information management (BIM) to the table to help eliminate construction waste.

Safety was of paramount importance and one of the key measures of success for the project. The use of Target Value Design was critical and is described in the construction chapter. We were able to add value-added enhancements from savings due to this methodology. Our building went up so fast we had to make certain to deploy transition planning (pull planning) early enough to be ready to occupy with our new processes.

The Finance and the Development Department were engaged from the beginning to plan the financing of the bonds and engage community partners to raise $50 million to support the project. Our internal Communications team was instrumental in keeping our staff and the community engaged in our building process.

The use of a construction website, regular publications, media engagement and a time-lapse camera kept stakeholders informed and made them feel as if the project was their own.

In the end, it was a collaborative project, a team effort described by team members in the following chapters, that delivered the promise of a new facility and our ability to continue to deliver family-centered care to the children and families we are proud to serve.

From The COO: Lessons Learned

- Don't sell your project short and reduce overall value by using only one lean methodology. The synergy of lean operations, lean design and lean construction will surpass your expectations. Consider a project methodology that matches your culture. If your culture is not one of collaboration, IPD may not be the best method. If your culture expects and values inclusion, IPD may be a good choice.

- Involve users. Involve users. Involve users. Don't expect clinicians, patients or family members to look at a schematic and decide if it will meet their clinical, operational and family needs. Most are not accustomed to thinking in 3-D.

- Users need to experience the space, see where the walls are that obstruct the vision of their patients and figure out how far they have to travel with a special-needs child in search of a bathroom.

- Appreciate the value that your project will bring to your local business and trades from the education in new methodologies. It will give them competitive advantage in the marketplace and provide benefit to other projects in your community.

- Plan to present a new methodology, such as ILPD, many times to stakeholders, particularly the executive staff and Board members. This is a significant and visible project, and they are responsible for ensuring successful completion. Their commitment and support are essential.

Building The Business Case:

Maintaining Family-Centered Care Amid Changes

By Grace Wakulchik, COO, and Jeffrey Hale, VP of Analytics and Performance Management

Akron Children's executive team needed to gain formal board approval to start the Tower Project, and employee and community buy-in to make the project successful.

The executive team built their business case upon historical and projected service data, and the latest clinical research and best practices. Each department had unique challenges and needs, but at the core of the business case was a drive to maintain the highest-possible quality level of family-based care to patients and patient families.

To support the family-centered business case, Akron Children's developed a five-year financial forecast. The forecast included an income statement, balance sheet, and key financial ratios. Using the projected volumes, we developed the income statement first. Although the income statement showed a dip in income from Operations during the first three years of the new building operating, it returned to target levels by year four. From the income statement, we forecasted the balance sheet and the key financial ratios. The key financial ratios stayed well within the acceptable limits.

Neonatal Intensive Care Unit (NICU)

NICU Overflow Days		
Years	Days	Overflow capacity
2010	72	20%
2011	141	39%
2012	152	42%

Looking at the needs of the NICU, the most obvious was that demand outweighed supply. Thirteen times from Aug. 10, 2010, to Jun. 23, 2014, we activated overflow NICU beds with approval from the Ohio Dept. of Health. Three times, the beds stayed activated for a stretch of more than 100 days.

We had tried to build private rooms with our existing space, but could get only 45. We just weren't going to have the capacity we needed with the space we had.

The other reason the NICU was targeted for improvement was that other hospitals —including local competitors — had transitioned to private rooms, a change that research on neonatal development supported to promote infection control, reduce length of stay and improve family satisfaction.

To continue to advocate for promotion of family-centered care, we had to have a facility that promoted it in our premiere service lines, which include neonatal intensive care. We had to have rooms where families could participate and be active partners in the care of their babies in the manner that we promote.

Private NICU rooms are proven to improve care. For example, they are quieter and more comfortable, which supports post-natal development. Further, light and sound can be adjusted for individual infant needs, thus improving neurological development. Research also proves that private rooms facilitate earlier physiological stabilization of preterm infants and enhanced maternal break-milk production.

Building Your Knowledge

Research, such as this study, supports Akron Children's determination that it needed to upgrade its NICU patient rooms to support family-centered care.

"Documenting the NICU Design Dilemma: Comparative Progress in Open-ward and Single Family Room Units"

Domanico, D., DK Davis, F. Coleman, and BO Davis.
Journal of Perinatology 31 (2011): 281-88. Print.

We included private bathrooms in the neonatal rooms as a patient initiative but also as lean initiative because we can convert the room to a pediatric intensive care unit or a regular in-patient bed if needed. We went with the idea of building flexibility.

Outpatient Surgery Center (OSC)

Outpatient Surgery Forecasts for ACH Main Campus

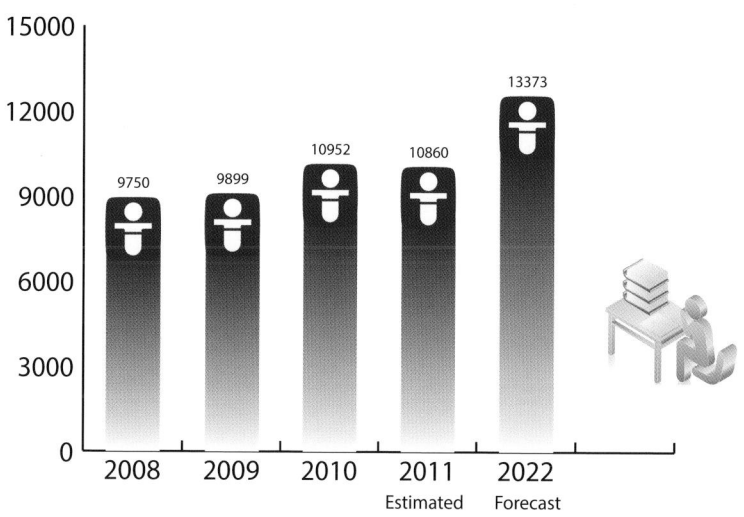

The number of outpatient surgeries is increasing as technological advancement enables less-invasive procedures that often don't require overnight stays. Historical data and forecasts show that Akron Children's is following this trend, and in building the business case, there was no shortage of anecdotal evidence that also showed that our surgery space wasn't keeping pace with change. Another important factor was that we had no additional block time in the surgery rooms to allocate to new surgeons.

Twenty pre-operative surgery rooms weren't enough to provide private rooms for patients as they waited, in gowns, to be prepped and taken to surgery. Patients and family members all waited together — 3-year-olds alongside 16-year-olds, girls alongside boys. This did not provide the best atmosphere for families or a confidential space for families to discuss their child's care with the surgical team.

Additionally, outpatient and inpatient cases were processed together, and so when an unexpected event disrupted the day's schedule, it affected all surgery patients.

From a lean perspective moving patients in and out of pre-operative rooms caused waste. We also had difficultly maintaining takt times for rapid turnaround of our outpatient surgery patients and wasted time continually tracking the location of patients.

With this project, we wanted to provide a very quick process for our outpatient surgery families. Often those procedures take 15 minutes, and we didn't want these quick turnarounds to be interrupted by an emergency case or a doctor being pulled away. We required a dedicated outpatient surgery center that would provide value to patients and families.

Building the new center provided other opportunities to improve patient experience and process efficiency and effectiveness:

- Post-surgery, patients will recover and be discharged from one area, instead of being moved to two different areas.

- By moving outpatient surgery elsewhere, the main surgery center recovered square footage, which will become a larger dedicated orthopedics operating room. An interventional radiology suite and inter-operative MRI suite are also planned for the backfill space.

- The hospital will be able to accommodate an increasing number of dental surgeries.

Emergency Department (ED)

Akron Children's ED had benefitted from ongoing process-improvement work since 2008, when the department began changing triage, check-in, check-out and other processes to improve throughput. The department transitioned from a "push" model of bringing patients into a room when the doctor was ready to see them to a "pull" model that used a green light signal to tell triage nurses that a room was ready for a patient.

But even with these changes, bottlenecks slowed down the flow and caused patients to wait. On weekends, the ED would sometimes be at "red light" (patients in the waiting room) for 70% of the time. A major choke point was the casting room, where kids with broken bones waited with their family sometimes for hours before getting a cast.

This waste screamed for improvement.

Trauma space in the current ED also could not support the growth in the Trauma Program. One of the three trauma rooms was so small that staff didn't use it for trauma cases. They used it for procedures that required sedation. The other two trauma rooms also were small, and so couldn't accommodate families and the volume of staff and equipment required.

Lack of visibility also was a problem. Staff couldn't see the activity in the trauma rooms from the main ED desk. Parents could not see providers or staff from their ED rooms and often wandered in the halls looking for staff.

The redesigned ED has three large-bay trauma rooms with a trauma support area. The trauma rooms were designed by the ED staff after running clinical scenarios to ensure optimum workflow for all caregivers. Twenty-three rooms are in the main ED, and there are 11 urgent-care rooms and three suture/procedure rooms.

The Behavioral Health ED is a successful program in the current ED, seeing around 14 patients per day. The team elected to duplicate this successful program in the new space to continue to meet the needs of our behavioral health patients.

Conclusion

Certainly the business case was important from a top- and bottom-line financial perspective, particularly for receiving a favorable bond rating and board approval. The underlying need, though, was the core belief in family-centered care that Akron Children's advocates. As healthcare technology and research change — and as the needs of the community change — hospital leaders know they must actively respond with capital and process improvements that are low in cost and high in quality and provide real value to our families and patients.

Education

Using PDCA To Level Understanding and Push Toward Perfection

By The Tower Project Education Team

Bernita Beikmann, AIA, EDAC, Director of Lean Strategy at HKS
David V. Chand, M.D, Physician COE Deployment Director at Akron Children's
Trauda Gilbert, COE Deployment Leader at Akron Children's
Will Lichtig, VP of Business and Process Development, The Boldt Co.
Nick Loughrin, Project Manager, The Boldt Co.

Ongoing learning — about customers, processes, ideas and each other — propels the lean-improvement engine.

Nothing will get better without education, and so the Tower project goal — reduce baseline space and cost needs by 20% without compromising quality — required ongoing education that needed to reach everyone who participated in the process.

The Tower project had specific challenges:

- large number of participants — about 300;

- high mix of participants (hospital employees from executives to clinic staff to maintenance team members); and,

- numerous design and construction professionals traveling in from out of town; as well as local contractors.

As the five-member education team, we assumed the responsibility of managing the education process. We used the PDCA method (plan, do, check, act/adjust) and the Plus/Delta assessment technique to continuously improve.

TIPS From The Trenches
Use Plus/Delta Assessment

In this technique, participants identify positive things as pluses, and things that should be changed as deltas. Using deltas instead of "cons" reinforces that learning is part of the continuous-improvement process. Almost every event during the Tower project ended with a Plus/Delta assessment of the event itself.

Sometimes, deltas need simple changes that can be done quickly, and so this technique also supports rapid improvement.

We served as instructors, as did other project participants, members of Akron Children's Center for Operations Excellence (COE), and external subject-matter experts.

Part 1: Lean Boot Camp

Akron Children's adopted lean principles in 2008, so some team members were familiar with lean concepts. Still, everyone needed some education. Only 20% of the 200 hospital team members had had training on a lean tool or concept; and, the COE would be introducing some concepts for the first time, such as the 7 Flows of Healthcare. Additionally, non-employee members on the IPD teams attended.

To bring everyone's knowledge to an equal level, we designed a two-day Lean Boot Camp based on the 5 Principles of Lean, as outlined by James Womack and Daniel Jones in their book, *Lean Thinking: Value; Value Stream; Flow; Pull; and Perfection.*

Our vision was to create teams that would rely on lean fundamentals as they made decisions about their future workspaces. We included all vice presidents, directors, managers and supervisors who the Tower project would affect, and everyone who had been appointed to the design teams for the three departments.

Building Your Knowledge

James Womack and Daniel Jones

Womack and Jones co-authored a series of books that are considered the foundation of modern practical application of lean principles to organizational/project structure and management. Womack, Jones and co-author Daniel Roos introduced the term "lean" in the 1991 book *The Machine That Changed The World* to describe the ultra-efficient management principles that were silently propelling Toyota Motor Corp. past the world-dominating Big Three automakers.

Womack and Jones continued to work together at the non-profit Lean Enterprise Institute (www.lean.org) to study and teach lean principles to manufacturers and then, subsequently, to countless other types of businesses and organizations.

Figure 1: Lean Boot Camp Agenda

Day 1

Seeing value through the eyes of a child

Developing eyes for waste

Waste walk

Understanding the value stream

A3 thinking

Day 2

Understanding flow and pull

Demand, takt time and work leveling

5S: Sort, Straighten, Shine, Standardize, Sustain

Standard work instruction and visual management

Daily management system

Recap and how what was learned will apply to the lean design process

Expectation of lean design teams

Group discussion

The first step was to develop an outline of content material. We used lectures combined with simulations or activities to teach each principle, the classic learn-and-apply technique for lean education.

Day 1: Value, Waste, Problem-Solving and Understanding Mapping

TIPS From The Trenches:
Stick To the Basics

Using the 5 Principles of Lean to structure curriculum provided a pre-configured introduction to the "big ideas" behind lean. Another benefit is that the principles can be conveyed with inexpensive and fairly fast simulations.

5 Principles of Lean

1. Identify Value
2. Map the Value Stream
3. Create Flow
4. Establish Pull
5. Seek Perfection

Value

Specifying value from the perspective of the customers — the patient, the patient family and hospital staff — was the first lesson.

We asked participants to "see" the new building through the eyes of the patient and patient family. We instructed them to use more than a visual picture and to specify how they would feel and what they would hear in the new building.

The team members wrote ideas on Post-It Notes and then placed them on separate boards for patients, parents and staff. The instructors asked them to identify recurring themes. We used Wordle™ to depict the most frequently used words.

A Wordle™ documented recurring themes early on in a discussion of value.

Waste

In a lean organization, identifying waste is as important as identifying value, so we used three activities to teach team members to identify waste.

Video: *Toast Kaizen*, by two-time Shingo Prize recipient Bruce Hamilton, which illustrates the waste present in the mundane tasks of toasting and buttering bread.

Waste Walk: Team members formed groups and toured specific areas of the hospital. We asked them to take note of examples of waste using the DOWNTIME acronym. The small groups then reconvened, presented their observations, and then recognized recurring themes, i.e., DOWNTIME.

The goal of the waste walk was for participants to begin to see waste in their processes and develop a vision for the future.

DOWNTIME = Waste

At Akron Children's Hospital, the acronym "DOWNTIME" is used to remember the eight types of waste:

1. **D**efects
2. **O**verproduction
3. **W**aiting
4. **N**ot Using Employee Talent
5. **T**ransportation
6. **I**nventory
7. **M**otion
8. **E**xcess Processing

Spaghetti Diagrams: Finally, the team used spaghetti diagrams and the 7 Flows of Healthcare. Spaghetti diagrams, which often use department blueprints, provide a visual representation of the paths employees take as they work. They highlight the two most common forms of waste in hospital processes — motion and transportation.

7 FLOWS OF HEALTHCARE

1. Patients
2. Family
3. Staff
4. Medications
5. Equipment
6. Supplies
7. Information

By visualizing how these seven flow in the current state, the team members began to see how the future state could work to remove unnecessary motion and transportation.

Value Stream Mapping

The value stream is a diagram that outlines the major steps in a process, shows how information is exchanged, and contains a large amount of data about time and resource utilization. Understanding how to create and interpret a value stream was an important objective, as each team would be responsible for this task for its respective service line during the design process.

To practice, teams were given a video of a lab process to observe and then develop a value stream map.

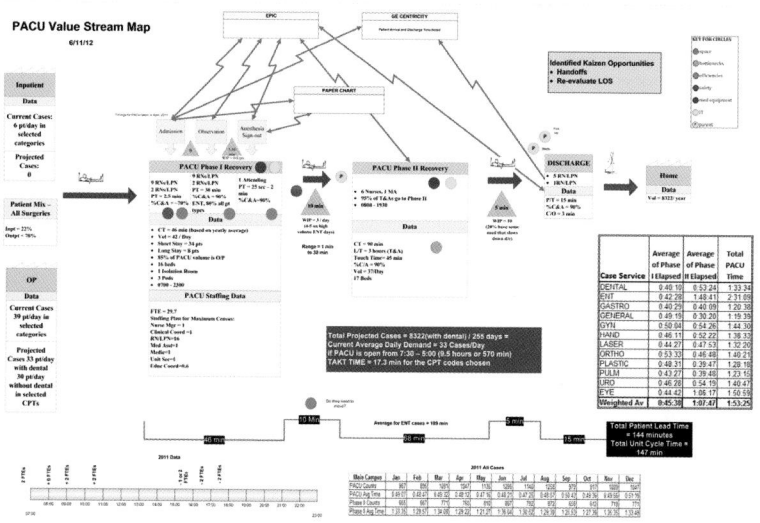

Building Your Knowledge

A3 Document

An A3 document is named after the 11-by-17-inch-sized paper (called A3 in some parts of the world) that Toyota engineers used to summarize problem-solving exercises, status reports and impending plans. Often, A3s contain photographs and other visual elements.

Generally, there are four quadrants to record: background, current condition, desired condition and implementation steps.

Next, we gave a lesson on using an A3 problem-solving document and had teams produce an A3. We learned that the boot camp setting provides only enough time to introduce the basic A3 concept. We did not have the team produce complete A3s, but we did have them do some pen-to-paper mocking to encourage them to use clear, critical thinking when evaluating a problem and use the concepts of background, current state, etc.

Day 2: Flow, Pull and Seeking Perfection

Dot Card Game

The Dot Card Game is a well-known simulation where teams are asked to create a production line creating cards with dots and stamps. Teams begin with specific instructions whereby product is batched between steps. Work done by members of the team all have varying process times. The team then develops multiple iterations until they improve the process to create flow.

The concepts learned in this simulation were important because they applied not only to hospital operations, but also directly to how the Tower would be designed and built: recognizing batches, the importance of flow, and understanding quality in the eyes of the end customer.

It was also important for team members to understand the concept of takt time because it was being used to calculate the number of rooms.

Building Your Knowledge

Takt Time

According to the Lean Enterprise Institute's Lean Lexicon, the German aircraft industry first used takt time in the 1930s to manage production. Takt is German for a precise interval of time, such as a music meter. In lean product/process planning, it is calculated as available time (one shift, one step, one cycle) divided by customer demand, i.e., how many you need to make or serve to fulfill need.

Seeking Perfection

The COE offers various training programs on tools for seeking perfection: daily management, standard work instructions (SWI), 5S and visual management. In this condensed version, we shared examples, including photographs, to illustrate how these tools have been used successfully at Akron Children's.

Examples included:

- SWI for helicopter pilots to follow before take-off and after landing
- Daily huddle boards and huddle best practices
- Use of visual management to improve the ability to locate items in the Sterile Processing Department

Putting It All Together

Participants used Mr. Potato Heads in a wrap-up simulation.

Being a children's hospital, it was only appropriate for us to use toys in our simulations. The COE had already developed a simulation using Mr. Potato Head for A3 training for frontline staff, so we had some of these supplies readily available. (With class sizes going past 30 individuals in a session, we had to buy out Amazon's available inventory of Mr. Potato Heads in order to accommodate several simulation teams simultaneously.)

The group was divided into teams of equal size. We ran three rounds of the simulation, allowing teams to improve on their performance by applying lean principles they had learned: understanding customers value, 5S, visual management, error-proofing, understanding the current state, process time, lead time, calculating takt time, building to customer demand, creation of a load chart, right-sizing resources and development of SWI.

The competition kept the event fun and entertaining. It was a great end to two days of work.

Part 2: Lean Design and Construction Education

The education process continued into the design phase, when more non-hospital employees began participating. Akron Children's, Boldt, and HKS created a strategy for education that started with a Lean Boot Camp for contractors and continued into specific learning units as the design process progressed.

Creating a Shared Mind

A team consisting of hospital team members, design and construction team members and users was the first team, and we called them a Study Action Team (SAT). A facilitator led the team through reading and discussing the book *Product Development for the Lean Enterprise* by Michael Kennedy. The SAT's goal was to develop a broad understanding of lean applied to our work, and to ultimately develop a strategy for Target Value Design (TVD).

TIPS From The Trenches:
The Benefit of a Book

Reading a book as a group instead of just having a work session enables the team to relate to a story and discuss it in a forum that allows people to speak freely and learn from each other because it is non-threatening. This experience also promotes team building through common understanding.

Building Your Knowledge

Here are three books on lean design:

Product Development for the Lean Enterprise,
By Michael N. Kennedy

Ready, Set, Dominate: Implement Toyota's Set-Based Learning,
By Michael N. Kennedy and Kent Harmon

Lean Product and Process Development,
By Allen C. Ward

Target Value Design

Building Your Knowledge

Target Value Design (TVD) is a management practice that focuses on value to the customer through the design process and recognizes the importance of constraints. The most significant constraint is usually cost, but others occur as well. TVD offers designers an opportunity to engage in design conversation concurrently with those people who will procure and execute the design. For more information on TVD, see the Contract section in the Appendix.

The project-delivery process called for innovation in designing both process and product. The contract specified that we would use Target Value Design (TVD) to facilitate this innovation.

Some team members had no TVD experience, and some had limited experience with how TVD would be used in this project. We needed to create a structure to bring everyone's TVD knowledge to the same level.

We used a simulation called "Flip the Tarp," to emphasize the power of constraints. We asked team members to figure out a way to turn a tarp over that they were standing on without moving off of it. After they accomplished the task, constraints were added. They actually performed better with the constraints on their second try.

Constraints make us better at what we do. They make us more innovative and creative. This exercise allowed the participants to start to examine that concept.

Design Thinking

We used a segment from ABC's *Nightline* on the IDEO shopping cart as a primer for design thinking. IDEO is a global design firm that created the shopping cart to demonstrate its design process for the segment.

The IDEO design process uses cross-functional teams, sometimes teams designing to one quality or design feature, brainstorming every crazy idea that they have. This video allowed the team members to think about different methods of design thinking without traditional barriers. What happens when you design only for one condition of satisfaction? What happens if all of your team members are not design experts? It showed how a company that does not claim to be an expert in the design of any particular thing manages to design innovative products.

The Marshmallow Challenge gave team members insight into the power of prototyping. We gave teams of seven a few simple materials and asked them to build the tallest structure they could that would support a marshmallow. The exercise was also a team-building experience where the talents of engineers, architect, constructors were challenged on building a structure. At the conclusion they found out that often, kindergartners do a better job than adults. Why? They work together, focus on the end goal, and they prototype. They build and test many different things in order to get the best solution.

Looking at multiple options, even if many are rejected, is important in any decision. Sometimes a failed option will provide an idea about a better solution.

Adjustment: How Education Improves

Adjustment was most important in the design phase because intense interaction was required to push innovation in problem solving. (In the PDCA cycle, A can be "adjust" as well as "act.")

Giving awards might seem silly, but it helped make Team Week report-outs more efficient and fun. This award rewarded teams for using "pull" methods instead of "push."

We checked in with each other frequently to discuss what was working well and what was not working well. We used experience and education to adjust methods.

We would educate to a certain extent in the Big Room, and then we would gauge weekly whether the things we had taught were working the way we wanted them to, and if they weren't, we would adjust. Sometimes we would do little bits of education throughout the Big Room, and sometimes we would add a facilitator to teams.

In one case, when the teams were not interacting enough, we adjusted an Innovation Team's structure to have an administrator and a project leader to facilitate teamwork.

Another example was Team Week report-outs. Plus-Delta feedback was that they were taking too long and were not providing value for the time commitment.

We recognized that the problem was that people didn't understand what they had to do and were not coming prepared, so we changed the rules. We told everyone they had to gather in the front of the room with no laptops and phones, and they had to present their progress and answer a small number of questions quickly. And then we started giving out small awards, like one for meeting goals. We also had one for best report-out, and soon we had people rapping their report-outs and dressing in costumes.

It sounds a little silly, but what it did was make people focus a little more on what they were doing. And those report-outs went from taking two hours to about an hour, and they were more meaningful.

These adjustments changed outcomes from unacceptable to acceptable and demonstrate that, like all aspects of a lean project, participants must respond to improvement cues as they are revealed or recognized. Otherwise, triggers and flows that make lean projects so successful won't happen.

Project Management

Collaboration, Concurrent Processes Propel Teams Toward Goals

By the Owner's Project Management Team (Lin Gentile, VP/Construction & Support Services, Akron Children's; Cliff Greive, Director of Construction, Akron Children's; Ray Walker, Managing Director and Stephen Powell, Consultant for CBRE Healthcare)

The Tower project was Akron Children's first major capital-improvement endeavor since executives and board members chose lean/Six Sigma as the hospital's strategic engine, so it was obvious to leaders that lean/Six Sigma would also drive the Tower project's execution plan.

Project Delivery Decision

In construction projects, Project Delivery Method is the approach used to:

1. Select team members to work on the project.

2. Contract with those team members.

3. Execute the design, construction and completion of the project.

Clearly, we wanted to eliminate waste and create innovative opportunities in constructing the Tower project. The first decision we faced was determining the best option for a Project Delivery Method. We selected the Integrated Project Delivery (IPD) method over traditional methods such as Design-Bid-Build or Construction Manager at Risk because IPD includes components of lean/Six Sigma and innovation. We also liked that using IPD would allow for the Owner to bring on design and construction partners early in the project to help carry the project structure forward.

Forming this team early would also be instrumental in structuring the IPD contract, thus the IPD Team. This relationship created a more streamlined, functional and successful project team that would benefit all parties involved, as well as the project.

Selection of IPD Team

Above and to the right: Hospital teams were deeply involved in choices made for allocation of space, flow, equipment and furniture.

Selecting the IPD Team was next. We looked for experts in using IPD while maintaining a goal of educating the community through the project effort. We selected a local representative, Hasenstab, to assist with design prior to seeking experts from across the country. The search nationwide led to the engagement of HKS, which had moderate experience in national IPD projects. Keeping with the same idea of educating the community, we selected Welty Building Company as the local contractor prior to seeking an industry leader in IPD. By selecting Boldt, we not only found an expert in IPD, but also a firm with a strong lean background, which would complement Akron Children's goal of using lean/Six Sigma methods throughout the project.

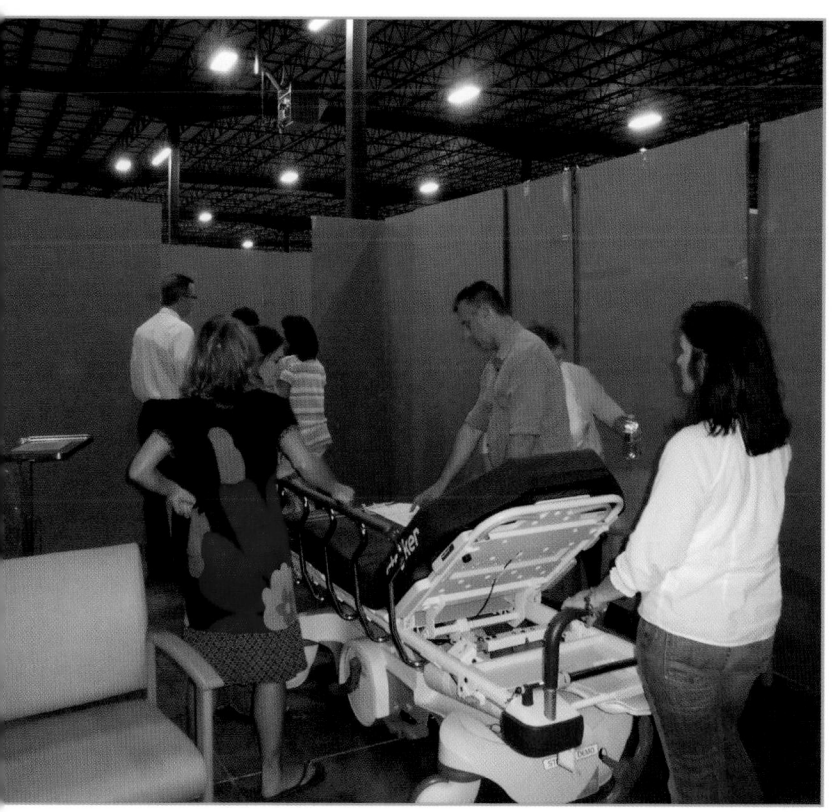

Teams Empowered To Drive Project Goals

With the groundwork in place, this IPD Team was tasked with creating the management structure for the project, a crucial component of the execution plan. The Owner's Project Management Team was not to be the final decision makers for the project. The IPD team would share in decision making on all items for the project. This would mean that the IPD team would have the final say on all items project related; therefore an appropriate team hierarchy would need to be established.

The Tower project's teams included:

- **Senior Executive Team (SET):** This group included executives from the Construction team, Design team, and Owner (the hospital). Members met once a month. Members looked out for the project as a whole but didn't manage it. They were there for support, not direction. The team also provided the final decision in the event the PLT could not make a unanimous decision.

- **Project Leadership Team (PLT):** Members met three times a week and were responsible for the decision-making and management of the overall project. The team consisted of: three representatives from the Owner; two from the Design team; and two from the Construction team.

- **Innovation Teams:** These teams were responsible for singular aspects of the project: Site, Structure, Interior Design and Architecture, Mechanical/Electrical/Plumbing, Exterior, Technology and Medical Equipment, and Production.

The SET and PLT were to be the committees responsible for managing all major decisions on the project with Innovation Teams being responsible for their respective areas of design and construction.

The intent of the Innovation Teams was to take pieces/parts of the project and focus on them to increase productivity, value and delivery. The collaboration was very intense during the design phase because Construction and Design were working together to improve the quality of the design while simultaneously driving down costs.

IPD Advantages and Disadvantages

Agreement

Advantage: The project agreement aligns the interests of the Owner, contractor and design team through the use of incentives and shared risk to better the project outcome; and it creates a formal contract that is signed by all five parties. This limits finger-pointing as the team is in it together.

Disadvantage: Although the owner ultimately has overall control of the project, the agreement provides an enhanced level of control to the architect and contractor, with the idea that a core group of team members should agree on any major issue before the project proceeds on that issue.

Schedule

Advantage: Construction can begin in a phased approach, thus compressing the project schedule because packages can be developed early.

Disadvantage: There are up-front costs that don't exist in other methods, such as insurance and user design pre-construction costs.

Estimating and Costs

Advantage: Estimating as you go and designing to target costs creates opportunities to identify budget issues as they occur as opposed to at selected project milestones. Budget-as-a-design-criteria is a major element to this approach.

Disadvantage: Similar to the Design-Build method, decisions are pushed up in the process due to the early commitment of pricing. This puts pressure on the Owner.

Subcontractors

Advantage: Integrating key subcontractors early allows the opportunity to provide design assistance, value engineering and other early services that can save money and improve the schedule.

Disadvantage: Integrating key sub-contractors early means they may be selected on qualifications and feeds and not hard bid as in traditional methods.

The Big Room

The teams needed to find an effective way to communicate and collaborate with other members, who were from all over the country. The idea of creating an environment for the Innovation Teams to co-locate became a priority. Having these teams work together in this environment would carry forward the IPD goals and keep a constant focus on the big picture, i.e., a successful project for all involved. Most of the work took place in The Big Room, a room large enough for all team members to gather and/or work as individual teams in designated spaces. The Big Room was in a hospital building that had lots of wall space for visual communication and collaborative facilitation of tools.

The Innovation Teams collaborated and planned work based on input and feedback from "customers," i.e., hospital employees, patients and patient families who had attended town-hall meetings, simulated scenario sessions and/or design mock-ups. When the Innovation Teams couldn't agree on how to solve a problem or needed high-level approval to move forward, they would consult the PLT team on-the-spot through the A3 decision-making process.

Some work was done during off-weeks outside of The Big Room, but even during this away time, facilitators and team members used tools to stay connected so that work moved forward unimpeded.

TIPS From The Trenches:
Solving Problems Quickly

The Big Room enabled two principles of lean design that speed up the design process: comprehensive and focused decision-making early in the process, instead of the crafts/technicians working in isolation and then later addressing conflicting decisions; and concurrent processes, i.e., teams working simultaneously instead of with hand-offs back and forth and between steps.

During Team Weeks in the design phase, 50 to 70 team members (some local; some traveling from from out of town) would co-locate in The Big Room on Tuesday morning to Report In and finalize the week with a Report Out on Friday morning. After the design phase, the meetings changed to once a month in person and once a month virtually.

The teams would set the agenda for the week together on Tuesday. The Innovation Teams drove the agenda based on the projects they were working on. The intent was to get to complete solutions and then execute them the following week without a lot of email and phone calls back and forth.

It was set up so that when team members went back to their offices, they had work to do, but they could have a heightened level of focus due to the collaboration from Team Week.

Lean/Six Sigma Tools

With the engagement of all parties and the creation of teams, several Lean/Six Sigma tools were used for managing the project. Here are three that were invaluable:

Connected Decision Huddles: In the off weeks from Team Week, the teams used Connected Decision Huddles, which were 15-minute calls every Tuesday, Wednesday, Thursday and Friday. The Innovation Teams would check in to see if there were any issues that had to be elevated to PLT. The huddles provided a structure for work without the teams being physically together every week.

Choosing By Advantages: When making decisions between multiple viable options, teams used Choosing By Advantages, which is a decision framework that seeks the best option by asking: *What are the advantages of each choice? How important are the advantages to "customers"?* and *Are those advantages worth their associated cost?*

A3 Documents: The teams used A3 documents, a foundational lean tool, to identify the root cause of a problem/obstacle and then determine the components of a complete solution. This also allowed for information to be detailed from Innovation Teams that could be reviewed and approved by the PLT. These documents lined the walls of The Big Room during the most intense periods of design collaboration. To see some examples of the A3s the teams used, see the Appendix.

Building Your Knowledge

For more information on Choosing By Advantages, read *The Choosing by Advantages Decisionmaking System* by Jim Suhr.

Innovation Team members working on problem-solving in Mission Control.

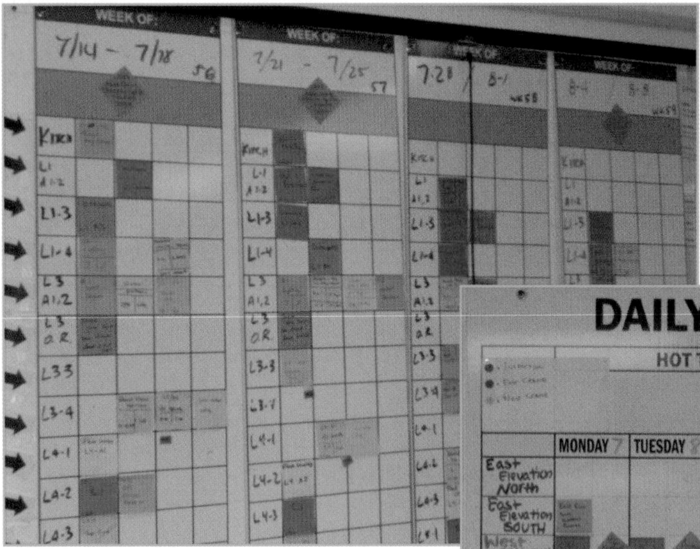

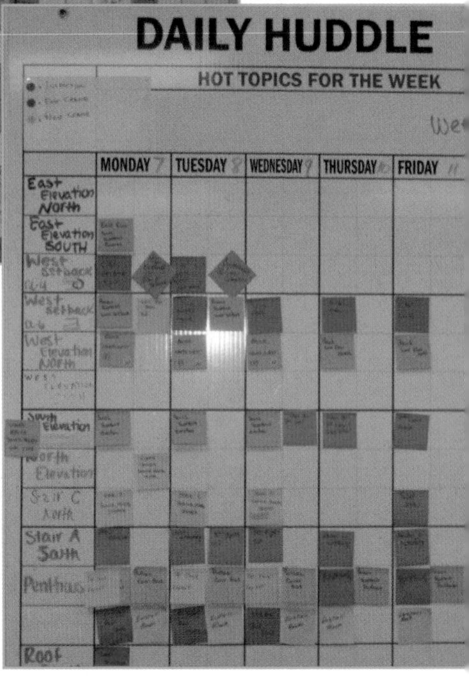

Mission Control was in a building adjacent to the Big Room where visual tracking for the project was posted in multiple ways.

DAILY HUDDLE

HOT TOPICS FOR THE WEEK

PULL PLANNING:
Keep The Train Moving!

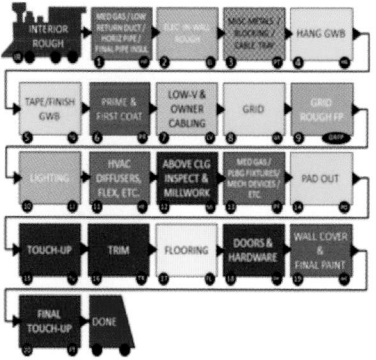

We used a train visual to manage a pull plan for the construction project schedule. In a traditional project, trades work in batches, with one trade completing their work, then another completing their work, etc.

The pull plan enabled concurrent process so that the construction timeline was shortened and collaborative problem-solving could occur instead of stopping work to solve problems as each trade encountered them during their timeslot.

The construction teams would use the train visual to plan work based on the "pull" of the preceding team's work. When a team finished in one area, they moved to the next, with the next "train car" following based on the Reliable Promise made of when the preceding "train car" would be done. Touch-Up would say, for example, we will be done in two days. The trim team could then plan their current work to finish in two days so they could move to the site that Touch-Up was finishing.

For a more detailed description on Reliable Promising, see the Appendiix.

 E³ **Engagement, Everywhere, Everyone**

Bakers for Builders:
All hospital staff members were invited to bake three dozen cookies for the on-site construction workers. Once a month the baking team would deliver their cookies to the workers. Each baking staff member received a Baking for Builders t-shirt with this logo.

Lean Operations

Understanding Barriers and Envisioning Ideal Flow

By Sheryl Valentine, Lean Six Sigma Deployment Leader/Center for Operations Excellence, BSN, MBA, MBOE, BB, RN

At the start of every traditional building project, the energy and excitement focuses on the new design, but in an Integrated Project Delivery (IPD) project, the initial focus must be on the current state. *How does the department operate today?* is the first question to answer. Understanding the current operations includes a review of current volumes and processes, and identification of barriers within care processes in the current space through value stream mapping.

1. Define volumes: Initially, review the volumes of the last two to three years for an historical perspective but be sure to take into account any change in projected activity resulting from the move to the new space. Your senior leadership team will provide those numbers, usually developed by a consultant exploring growth opportunities and new potential in your service areas.

2. Map the current state to assess process flow and bottlenecks: Create a current-state value stream map of the department's processes to identify where they flow freely and where patients and staff encounter barriers. Those barriers are points where inventory is stacking up and waiting. This is a waste.

3. Discuss the current state and introduce envisioning of the ideal state: Bring the team together and talk about the department as it is today — the activity and barriers they experience daily. Once the team has agreement on how things really work, ask them to "see" their ideal state, what they would like the future to look like, and what they would change either in the facility space or in the work processes.

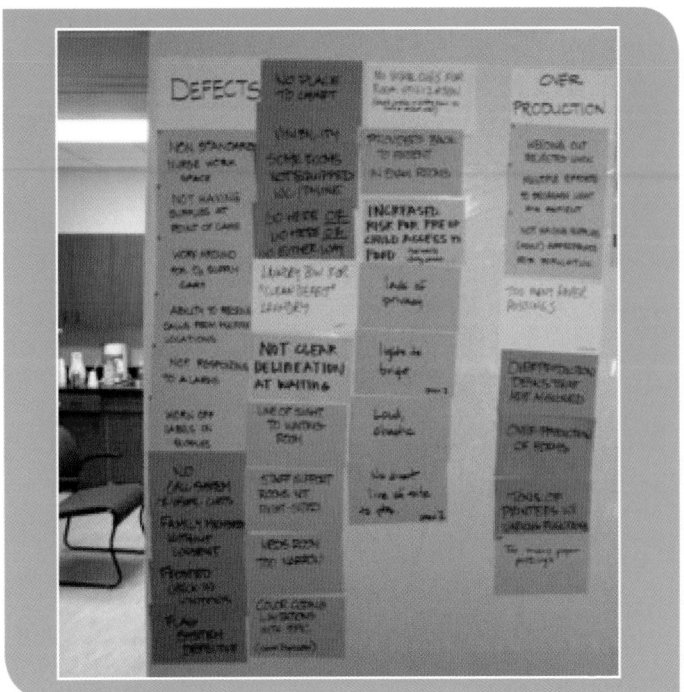

Identifying defects, one of the 8 Wastes of Healthcare.

4. Identify the gaps between the current- and future-state maps. This will help the team see what processes need to change and how the facility should be designed to support those new ideas. Consider using the *8 Wastes of Healthcare* to identify waste.

8 Wastes of Healthcare

1. Defects

2. Overproduction

3. Waiting

4. Not Using Employee Talent

5. Transportation

6. Inventory

7. Motion

8. Excess Processing

Create a future-state value stream map to capture that collective vision of an environment where the team's ideal flow can be achieved.

Current-State Value Stream Map For Emergency Dept. (ED)

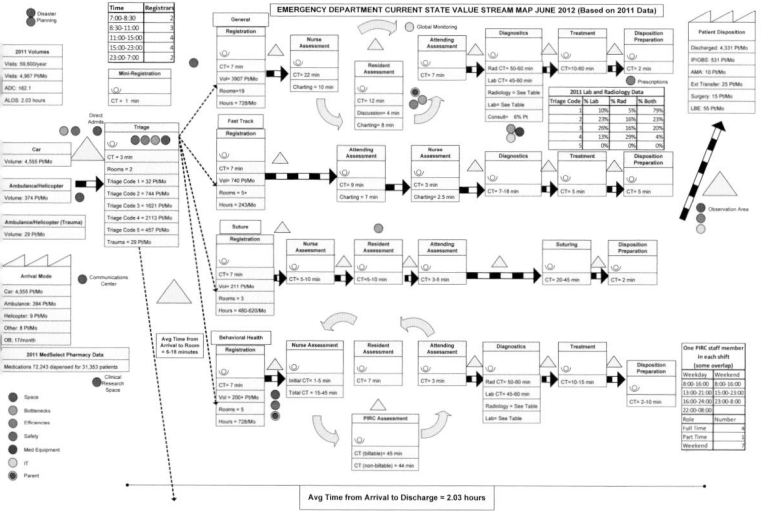

Future-State Value Stream Map For Emergency Dept. (ED)

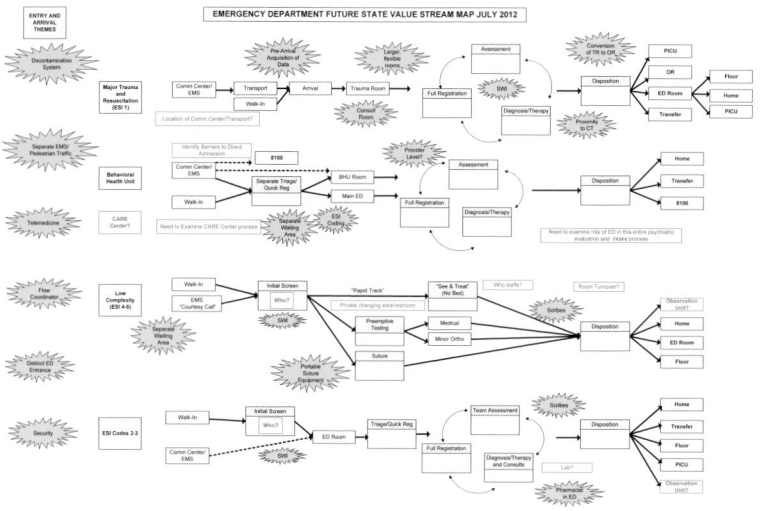

TIPS From The Trenches

Include All Who Touch The Processes

Be sure to include representation from all members of your team, from the providers to the clerical staff. Remember that those who do the work understand the work. That collective body of knowledge will make the project successful at all points of the value stream. Don't forget to include patients and families on the team. They provide a whole new perspective. Don't assume you know what they want.

Blocking and Stacking: If you are designing an entire building rather than a new department you can use this same lean technique to make sure that the departments involved are on the correct floor and the correct location within that floor for optimal patient flow.

5. Think about how the new space will support the processes needed to achieve optimal flow: The 3P Process (Preparation Production Process) will help the team to fine-tune their thinking. Let the *Seven Flows of Healthcare* guide your design.

7 Flows of Healthcare

1. **Patients**
2. **Family**
3. **Staff**
4. **Medications**
5. **Equipment**
6. **Supplies**
7. **Information**

In the 3P Process, you are using "paper dolls" or room cut outs that the team will arrange to help decide what rooms are needed and what are the most critical adjacencies to the flow of the work they are trying to achieve.

Ask the team what they need and provide the pieces they identify. You have done your room utilization calculation, so provide that number of patient care rooms. Let the team add or eliminate support rooms as the activity evolves into a design. That first pass will seem perfect! Take photos, document the design well and then dump it off the table. Ask the team to try it again, asking: *What did they learn with the first pass? What could they improve?*

This process requires seven passes before the design truly evolves. Architects will use the final iteration to prepare drawings for the full-size mockup.

TIPS From The Trenches

Don't Settle For Less Than 7 Iterations

Challenge the team to complete all seven iterations. Don't let them settle on iteration No. 1 or No. 2. Those always look "perfect" at first glance, but they can be improved. Urge the team to continue on using those identified gaps between current and future state to drive their design work. This is all about achieving lean operational excellence.

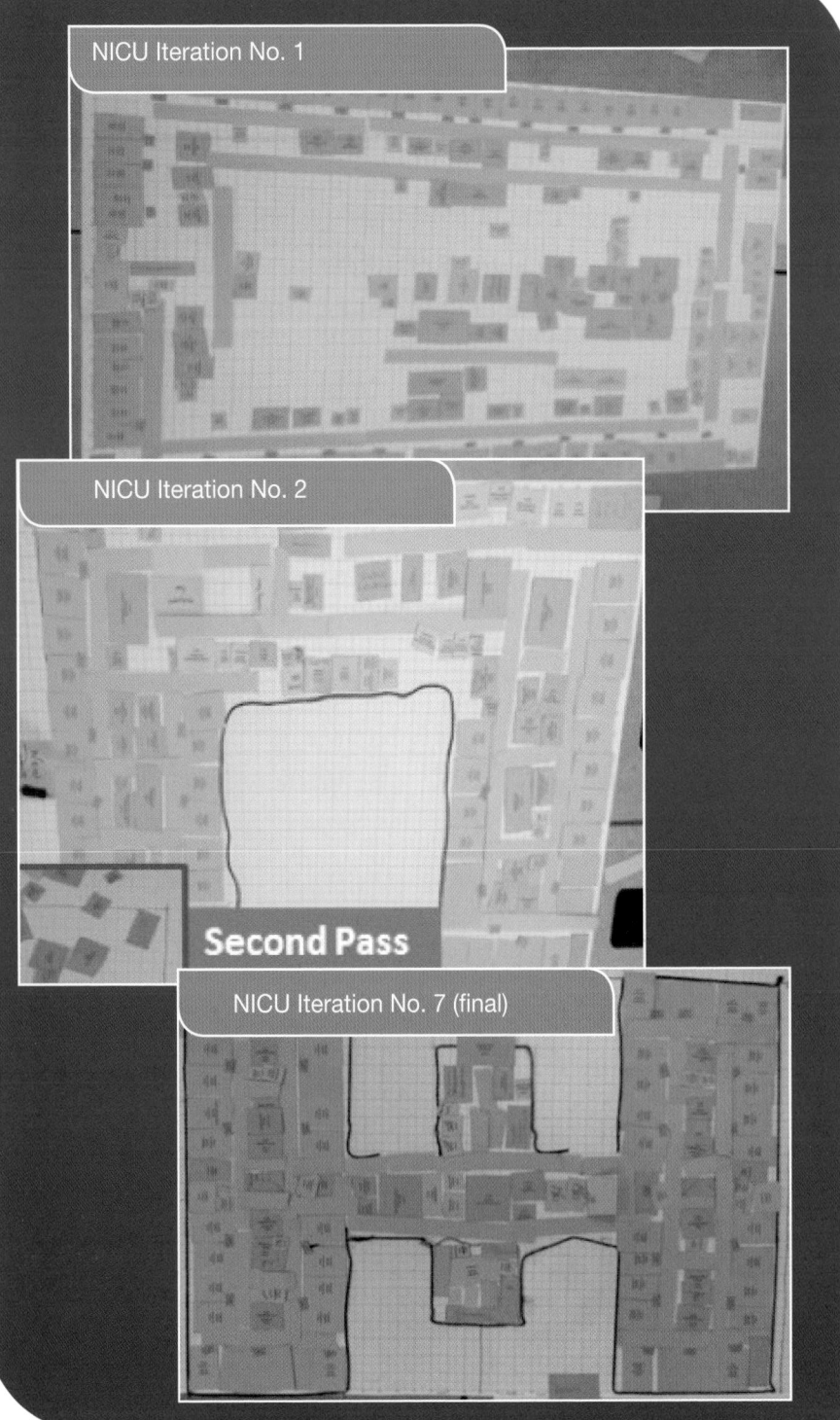

NICU Iteration No. 1

NICU Iteration No. 2

Second Pass

NICU Iteration No. 7 (final)

6. Test the space: Before the actual cardboard mock up sessions have the team create scenarios to test the space they have designed. Have them create a typical "day in the life" scenario, an emergency situation scenario, and a typical patient pathway scenario. Invite families to play their "role" on that day. Have fun and switch up the roles of the regular staff. That switch-up will result in a fun atmosphere and an environment of "fresh eyes." After each scenario is completed, use the Plus/Delta technique to explore what worked and what the team would like to see changed and re-tested.

A parent, a surgeon and three nurses working with the architect on a design change in the Outpatient Surgery Center based on a scenario learning.

As the team makes changes and decisions, be sure to document those decisions in an A3 format. This documentation is critical to the process work that still needs to be done and will help the team understand the decisions and why they are made, not only during this process but once the space is occupied and in use.

The architects are an integral part of this process and should be on site offering design alternatives for exploration as the learning occurs scenario to scenario. The architects also will keep the team out of trouble. They are the experts on local and state code requirements, life safety issues and just plain bad ideas. As the cycle of scenario, Plus/Delta, reconstruct and re-test occurs, the team will come closer and closer to their future state of optimal flow.

The metrics are important. Remember you are trying to reduce wasted transportation and motion as part of this process. Take current space and mock up measurements, and compare with each testing scenario. This may not be the most important driver of the design, but it should be considered in your efforts to reduce waste.

Building Your Knowledge

Resources for learning more on lean operations:

Jimmerson, Cindy, (2007), *A3 Problem Solving For Healthcare: A Practical Method for Eliminating Waste*, New York, Productivity Press

Rother, Mike & Shook, John, (2003), *Learning To See*, Cambridge, MA, The Lean Enterprise Institute

Wellman, Joan, Jeffries, Howard, Hagan, Pat, (2010), *Leading The Healthcare Journey: Driving Culture Change to Increase Value*, New York, CRC Press

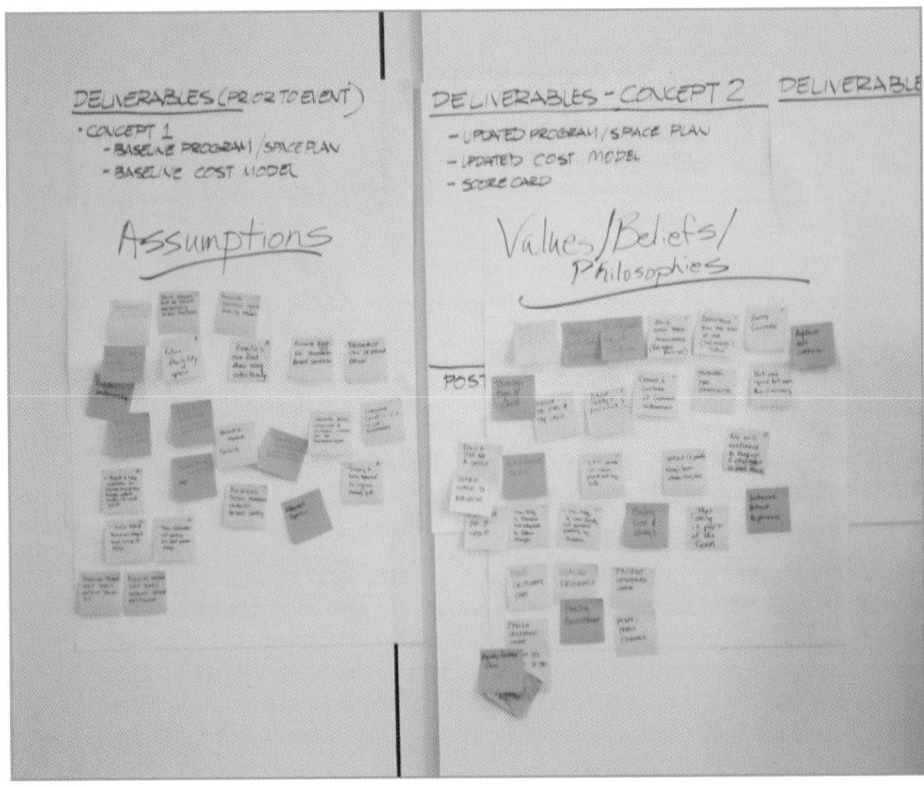

Use visual communication whenever possible during group sessions so that everyone is working from the same assumptions, beliefs and expectations.

TIPS From The Trenches

Encourage and Support Staff Participation

Bring support service staff to the mock-up sessions and encourage them to work through scenarios for their department and — in coordination with the clinical department — test them. Environmental Services, Food Service, Materials Management, Pharmacy, Lab, etc., are all part of the *Seven Flows of Healthcare*. Their input will be invaluable when it comes time to occupy the building as those services will have improved their service flows for the new space as well. The actual move to the new building will generate much less stress as the space is "known" and planned for by all the occupants.

7. **Address problematic areas:** Just because the actual design is finished, doesn't mean the work of the team is complete. The team worked to optimize the space to reduce ongoing staffing needs and that needs to be considered as the process work is undertaken. Move the team back to the value stream maps and work to smooth those processes identified as problematic. Keep the future-state map and the new floor plan handy. As new Standard Work Instructions are being drafted, refer to the floor plan. Keep a match between the team's vision of the new space and the Standard Work Instruction activities. Refer back to those A3 documents to review what the thought process was during the mock up revisions.

Divide the team into sub-groups assigned to work on individual and related processes. The original design team has the most knowledge about the new space, so they can become your steering committee for the operational work. The sub-groups can report back to the steering committee so the operational work and the vision for the processes of the new facility will stay in concert. Don't hesitate to bring other staff members on board who were not part of the original team. The more staff members involved in the process change, the better the understanding, and the higher the level of investment in the changes. High levels of ownership will result in higher achievement. The staff will want the changes to work, as they belong to them. This approach will also help mitigate some resistance to the changes. The more people know about the change, the less they will fear the change.

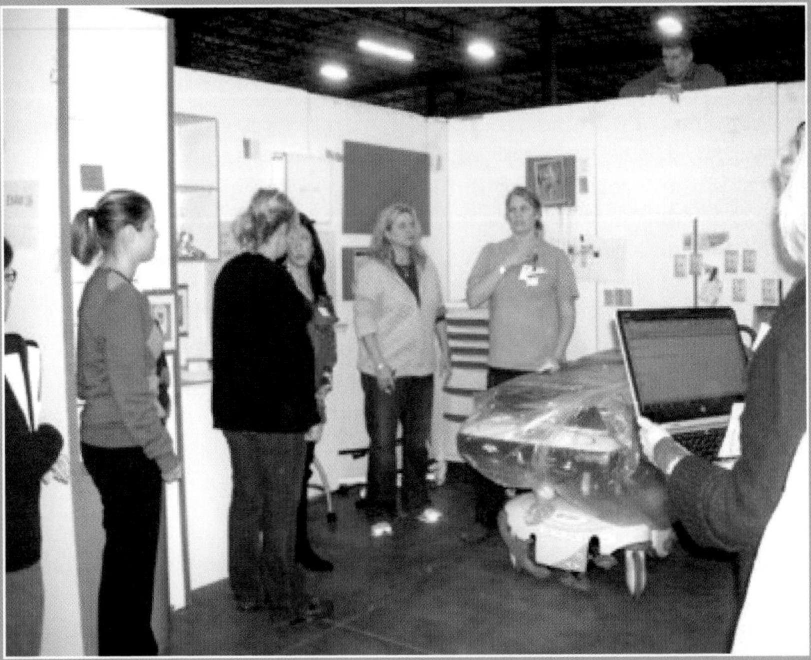

TEAMS AT WORK

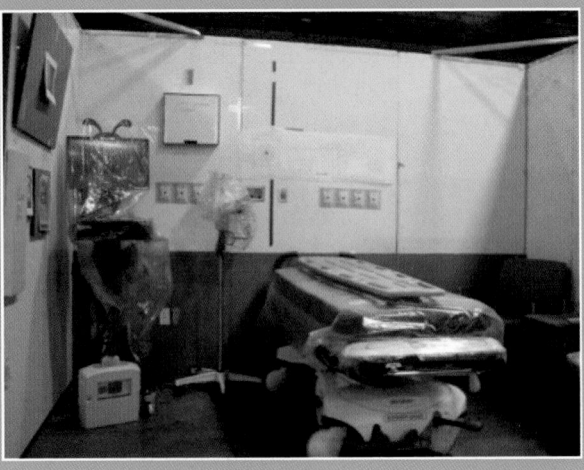

The ED Clinical design team works through a scenario in the trauma room: the medical director, physician, nurses and a parent as the architect looks down from above.

ED exam room

Team "building" the NICU headwall

NICU front desk

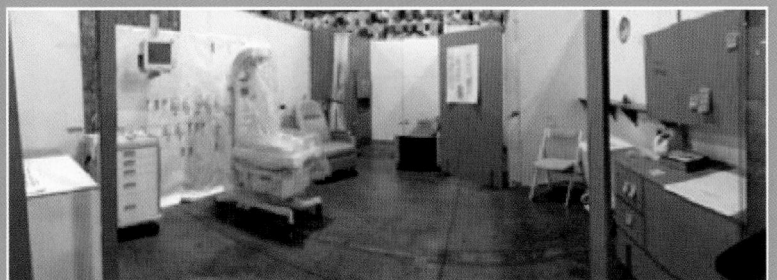

NICU single-family room

Lean Design

Facilitating User-Driven Decisions Within Project Goals, Safety Parameters

By the Design Team (John Bienko, AIA, Principal and Project Manager, HKS; Marge Zezulewicz, AIA, Project Manager and Medical Planner, Hasenstab Architects; and Scott Radcliff, AIA, Medical Planner, Hasenstab Architects)

The design process is perhaps the most disruptive component of the Integrated Project Delivery (IPD) model. Architects, interior designers and engineers are process facilitators — rather than process owners — and they use multiple sub-processes and tools during a series of week-long workshops to help users make detailed decisions, literally from ceilings to flooring.

In a traditional process, the design team usually works with a client administrator, financial manager, and two or three clinical managers who make up the client team. The traditional process starts with defining client needs and project constraints (i.e., budget, square footage, functions), and then the design team takes the lead on creating designs, which are vetted by the client team. In IPD, end-users make the design decisions for the client team based on their needs, which for Akron Children's included patients, patient families, and hospital professionals — clinical and support services.

This is a radically different way of working for design professionals, one that requires patience and humility as they work side-by-side with users, listening and learning what the users need to do their jobs and then challenging them to identify the best-possible design decisions that will provide the most value and use the least-possible resources to prevent waste.

Here are three examples of IPD practices that traditional architects likely haven't encountered before:

Working side by side (literally): Instead of working independently in offices and using the collective knowledge of colleagues to make decisions, we stood beside the hospital "customers" in the warehouse and observed and guided teams as they tested their collective knowledge and experiences with clinical scenarios. Throughout the process, users made the majority of decisions, and we suggested alternative options for process improvements. It was as if the user teams were given a kit of parts, and we were there to make sure they stayed within safety and viability parameters.

Educational site tours: For the majority of the hospital's user team members, this was their first encounter with facility design. To prepare the clinical team members for the week-long warehouse events, the hospital arranged site tours (also known in lean circles as gemba walks) to other pediatric hospitals that had recently completed new construction projects in similar clinical service lines. Whenever possible, they toured hospitals with a lean culture. Smaller groups — service line clinicians, a member from the Operations Excellence team and an architect — also took the tours, which gave the clinicians an opportunity to question and investigate operational and facility innovations that could be incorporated into their new departments.

Testing multiple design options: Constructing full size mock-up design solutions allowed the users to experience the space by physically walking through and testing multiple design options. The clinical team, families, and designers worked together to define which key adjacencies and features were critical clinical and environmental goals. For example, the ED team created and built two separate trauma configurations for scenario testing. By using a method called Set Based Design, where a range of options are developed to evaluate a range of desired capabilities, the users went through a process of measuring, analyzing, testing and improving several design configurations until they achieved their operational improvement goals. Ultimately, by enacting and learning from both trauma room configurations, the user team was able to blend best features from both into the design.

Warehouse Testing Roles And Responsibilities

Key processes for the design workshops include realistic clinical scenario testing and analysis. The user team members take on acting, observation and documentation roles of simulated clinical cases. After each scenario, the design and user teams identify benefits and improvement opportunities (Plus/Delta sessions) and chart the metrics for the scenario. A cycle of testing, analyzing, improving, re-building and re-testing is easily achieved in the warehouse environment.

Similarly, the design team members have specific roles and responsibilities during the workshop. Each service line (department) has a facilitator who is the master of ceremonies for the workshop. In the background, medical planners, clinical consultants and lean leaders work to document the process.

Comments and suggestions are captured for future discussions. Builders make modifications to the mock up structure and rearrange furniture and equipment to allow for quick re-evaluation by the user teams based on the findings of the previous scenario testing session.

As the initial clinical scenario is completed and evaluated, the user team gets a short break while the design team huddles to develop improvement strategies for the tested area. Once a strategy is defined, and — dependent on the complexity of required adjustments — some members of the design team create and modify the test area while the lead service line medical planner redirects the user group to the next clinical test or activity.

Building Your Knowledge

Heijunka Board

We initially used a structured schedule but found it was too limiting, so we started to use a "heijunka board" to give the design team appropriate time to respond to the user improvements and re-focus group activities. A heijunka is a visual guide that levels the quantity of work to be done over the time given. For more information, see *Lean Lexicon: A Graphical Glossary for Lean Thinkers*, published by the Lean Enterprise Institute, *www.lean.org*.

One role that remains a constant regardless of the approach, however, is the architect's responsibility for the health, safety and welfare of the occupants. The architect never relinquishes this responsibility and keeps the user teams out of trouble by identifying pitfalls and code violations and explaining best practice alternatives.

An example of this occurred in the Outpatient Surgery Center workshop when, after testing the original design, the PACU leaders requested full visibility within the unit for flexibility and staffing efficiencies. This request would have created building code travel-distance violations for exits. In response, we developed a strategy to create a "suite" for the PACU and reworked other attributes to achieve the open concept. The revised PACU and floor configuration were completely redesigned and tested by the clinical users within one day.

Encouraging Innovative Thinking

Challenging the user teams to reduce square footage while improving flexibility and efficiency within the workspace can be a delicate balancing act. Process improvements requested by the user teams can result cost increases. The team must also consider long term operating costs in terms of staff and supplies. We responded by incorporating Function Analysis Techniques (utilized by NASA) with the goal of obtaining the most economical solution that achieves the required functions. Numerous times we discussed "wants" versus "needs" when evaluating choices, and ultimately, the "want" items were placed on a value-add list that could later be incorporated into the design once the target construction cost was achieved.

The "pull" of cost reduction didn't mean always defaulting to the least-expensive option for materials, furniture, etc. Rather, we guided the teams with probing questions and encouraged them to use what they had learned in Lean Boot Camp (see Chapter 3 for more on Lean Boot Camp): Do you really need two of those? What does your takt time calculation tell you? Can you share one?

The workshop environment also provides a venue for the user teams to test actual building products and medical equipment. The construction team developed a real mock-up of the NICU observation windows so the staff could validate patient visibility during the Detail Design workshop. Similarly, the team took advantage of the OSC Detail Workshop to hold a vendor showcase where boom and integration representatives built and demonstrated their products for the surgical staff.

Design Phases

Concept Design (Similar to Pre-Design in Traditional Design) engages the user teams to identify their current state and identify their improvement opportunities through value stream mapping. The program of spaces is identified and vetted during this workshop phase. Once the program of spaces is vetted, a "paper doll," Rapid 3P session occurs to test and establish operational adjacencies on paper (see Chapter 5 for more details on the 3P session). Designers challenge the users to validate the layout with metrics. In preparation for Functional Design, the lead design facilitators meet with the user teams on a weekly basis to further develop their initial floor plan.

Functional Design (Similar to Schematic Design) pulls the user team members' experiences to create operational efficiencies by identifying key functional and space adjacencies. The week-long warehouse workshop incorporates rapid prototyping to build and test multiple layouts for the Seven Flows of Healthcare. Initial feedback from support-service representatives (in this case, nutrition, pharmacy, lab, environmental services, etc.) is requested to ensure all aspects of healthcare delivery are considered. A key goal at this step is to differentiate between "needs" and "wants." Design team leaders continue to meet with the user teams on a weekly basis to continue floor plan refinement and coordination with other floor plans in the building.

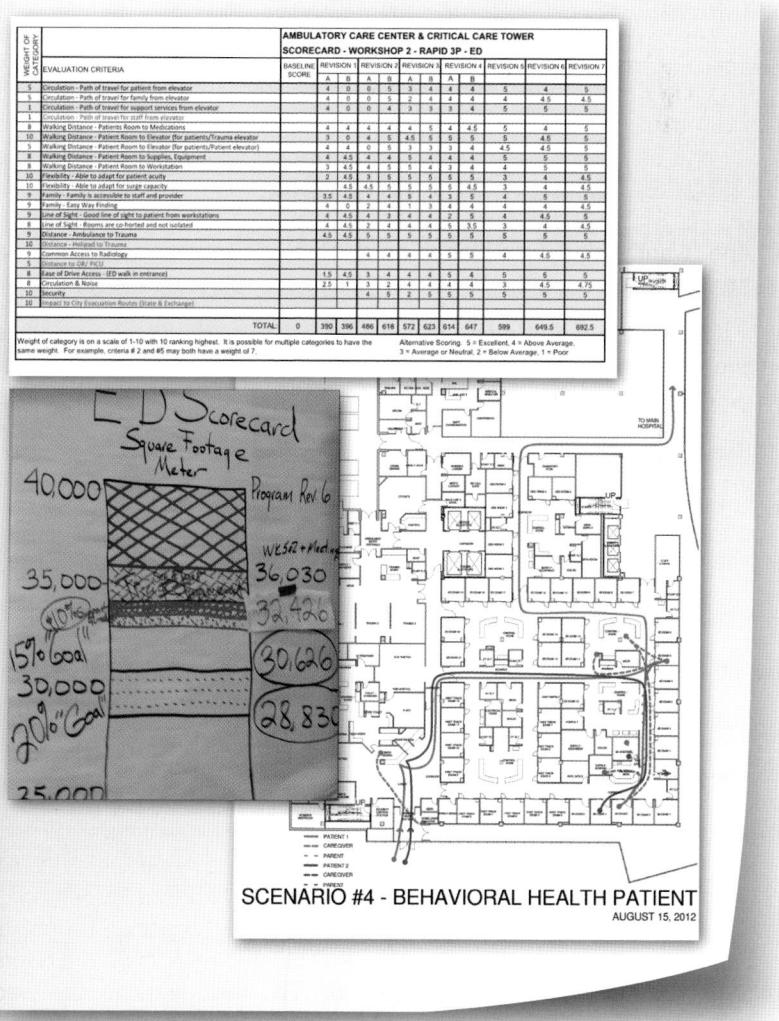

SCENARIO #4 - BEHAVIORAL HEALTH PATIENT
AUGUST 15, 2012

Detail Design (Similar to Design Development) identifies and tests the "in-room" features for each part of the unit. Once again, the week-long workshop uses rapid prototyping and actual furniture and equipment to define the ideal features and locations for patient, family and clinical amenities. The user teams also identify standard work procedures to be developed for their future new work environments. Representatives from the support services define their initial service concepts to the teams. The design team expands to include consultant and facility IT and medical equipment staff and representatives for all engineering disciplines to respond to all inquiries. Weekly design meetings continue, coordinating mechanical and electrical system distribution, code analysis and operational refinements with the user teams until the design is finalized. The user team's hard work is celebrated at the end Detail Design with design a sign-off celebration.

Implementation Documents (Similar to identified as Construction Documents Formatting) engages the designers and construction personnel to collaborate for final detailing of drawings and specifications. This phase documents all decisions for submission to the building department for plan approval and permitting.

Results: More Value For Patients, More Efficiency For Akron Children's

Here are examples of improvements that resulted from the warehouse design sessions:

- The final ED exam room sizes were reduced by 13% and offer flexibility for all patient types.

- Outpatient Surgery Center rooms were designed as "flex rooms" to allow overflow from PACU.

- NICU rooms were sized to accommodate any patient type to permit future flexibility.

Square Footage Reduction

	Square Footage for OSC	Square Footage for ED	Square Footage for NICU	Total Square Footage
Estimated using traditional building techniques	51,409	32,880	81,681	165,970
Final Lean Design	35,603	27,907	8,179	131,689
Difference	15,806	4,973	13,502	34,281

Through the IPD process, Akron Children's was able to reduce estimated square footage by more than 34,000 for the new Outpatient Surgery Center, Emergency Department and NICU.

Lessons Learned From the Design Team

- Create workshop committee to organize events.

- Place actual costs on equipment, furniture and construction materials to help users understand and consider costs.

- Be completely transparent with projected costs and the target cost for the project.

- Establish team rules and team guiding principles early in the session to help scope discussions and decisions.

- Deliver actual furniture, equipment and accessories to the warehouse early. This takes time to coordinate.

- Build cardboard kit of parts and 5S afterwards for re-use.

- Consult with clinical department leaders to plan realistic scenarios for testing.

- Use the 80/20 rule when evaluating options. Focus design time around the repetitive processes and scenarios which occur 80% or more of the time.

- Promote and transition facilitator leadership to the clinical staff as they emerge.

Lean Process –

2012

| APR | MAY | JUN | JUL | AUG | SEP | OCT |

PRE-DESIGN

Master Plan, Bootcamp & Site Visits

CONCEPT DESIGN

1 Future State / Visioning - All

2 Building / Stacking / 3P - All

FUNCTIONAL DESIGN

3 ED

4 OSC

5 NICU

6 OSC

Kaizen Workshops

2013

| NOV | DEC | JAN | FEB | MAR | APR | MAY | JUN | JUL |

DETAIL DESIGN

IMPLEMENTATION DOCS

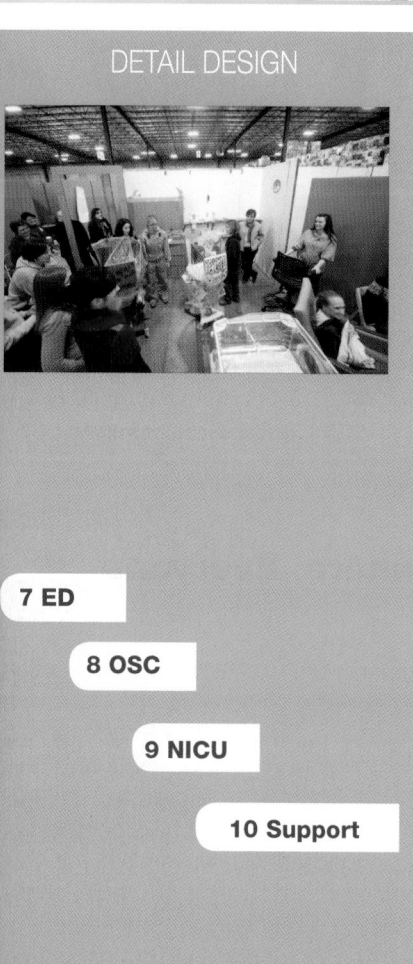

7 ED

8 OSC

9 NICU

10 Support

Akron
Children's
Hospital

Pictured L-R: Marge Zezulewicz of Hasenstab Architects; Sherry Valentine, an Akron Children's deployment leader; Grace Wakulchik, COO; and Scott Radcliff of Hasenstab Architects.

E³ Engagement, Everywhere, Everyone

Message of Hope and Community: Akron Children's design and construction team folded 1,000 origami cranes to signify hope and community. The cranes will be displayed at Peace Memorial Park in Hiroshima. "We were looking for a way to connect the building team to a story of compassion, and we thought of this wonderful story of Sadako Sasaki," said Norio Tsuchiya, vice president of HKS Inc. in Dallas, which was part of the Tower project. A survivor of the bombing of Hiroshima during World War II, Sadako was diagnosed with leukemia in 1954 as a sixth-grader. She began folding paper cranes in observance of the Japanese tradition that a wish will be granted upon folding 1,000 cranes. She wished for healing and peace. Sadly, Sadako died and fell short of her goal, but galvanized her community. They picked up on her cause and eventually built the Peace Memorial Park. Today, people and groups from around the world send batches of 1,000 cranes as a sign of their common wishes for peace and healing.

Lean Construction:

Learning, Trust, Teamwork, Predictable Workflow

Contributing: Will Lichtig, Vice President of Business & Process Development, The Boldt Company.

Construction projects are temporary "production systems" that historically have suffered from unreliable workflows. Unforeseen problems frequently plague field construction, so workers often are waiting on work; or completed work is waiting on workers at the next step. The unreliable workflows lower project safety, quality and productivity; and increase duration and costs.

Applying lean thinking to construction-project workflows has resulted in counter-measures that focus on production planning and control. As with any lean system, the production planning-and-control approach is described as a set of fundamental principles and basic practices that guide the development of a project-specific production system.

What follows is a description of the Akron Children's production system components. Note, though, that each construction project is unique. Leaders will need to evaluate their particular circumstances and determine how to apply the fundamental principles and basic practices to solve problems their project presents.

In order for the processes to be effective, project teams must develop and display:

- teamwork;
- trust;
- transparency; and,
- willingness to learn.

Figure 1: Boldt Approach To Lean Construction

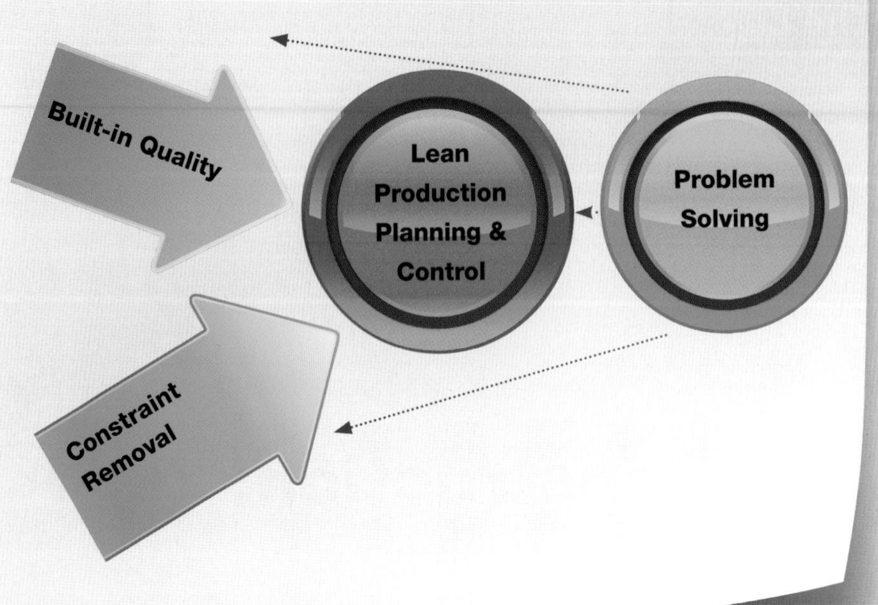

Figure 1 shows the basic elements of our approach to lean construction. At the heart is the basic Production Planning and Control process. Our approach is founded on The Last Planner System™ (LPS) and is augmented by takt planning. We have learned that in order for this process to produce reliable workflow, we also must implement a Constraint Identification and Removal Process to ensure that all obstacles are removed before work is released to the field for construction.

In addition, we must develop a Built-in-Quality process to ensure that the work, when installed, will meet the team's expectation without disruptive rework.

Finally, we understand that no system will likely produce perfection; hence the team needs a problem-solving process to both resolve issues that arise in the field and to systematically improve the other processes to avoid repeating problems.

Building Your Knowledge: The Last Planner™ System

The Last Planner System™ (LPS) is a production planning and control approach that is designed to produce predictable workflow and rapid learning. LPS is a collaborative, commitment-based planning system that integrates phase/pull planning, make-ready look-ahead planning with constraint analysis, weekly work planning based upon reliable promises, and learning based upon analysis of Planned Percent Complete (PPC) and Reasons for Variance.

Planning levels become progressively more detailed as the team gets closer in time to when the work will be performed. It begins with early-strategy conversations discussing how the work might be pursued and runs through commitment level planning by the lead individuals responsible for performing the work ("Last Planners"). Each planning cycle concludes with a review of actual performance compared with the commitment plan in an effort to promote learning and improve future reliability.

Understanding the Production System

The Boldt approach is grounded in The Last Planner System™, a production management-and-control system designed to produce rapid learning and predictable workflow. It contains multiple planning levels, which become progressively more detailed as the project's groundbreaking approaches.

It begins with early discussions of contract milestones and runs through daily planning by the leaders responsible for performing the work (Last Planners).

The planning cycle concludes with a review of actual performance compared with the commitment plan in an effort to promote learning and improve future reliability and worker productivity. The levels in the planning system are: Master Schedule; Phase Planning; Production Strategy; Look-Ahead Planning; Weekly Work Planning; and Daily Huddles.

Level 1: Master Schedule

The Master Schedule captures primarily "hard" contract milestones and integrates the IPD team's collaboratively developed general approach to design and construction. Milestones might include permit-package submission, permit-issuance dates, project dry-in, Construction Complete, and Owner Occupancy.

These are milestone dates that can't be compromised and so drive the timing of the various project phases, which the Master Schedule also delineates.

Project Construction Schedule Major Milestones

CCT Tower Schedule Activity	Duration	Start	Finish
1) Foundations	13 Weeks	6/24/13	9/20/13
2) Super Structure	33 Weeks	8/12/13	3/28/14
3) Mechanical/Electrical Rooms & Vertical Risers	26 Weeks	11/18/13	5/16/14
4) Enclosure Backup & Roof	28 Weeks	11/25/13	6/6/14
5) Main Distribution Overhead	30 Weeks	12/2/13	6/27/14
6) Framing & Rough-Ins	28 Weeks	2/10/14	8/22/14
7) Enclosure Finishes	33 Weeks	3/10/14	10/24/14
8) Finishes	50 Weeks	3/10/14	2/20/15
9) Landscaping	16 Weeks	8/4/14	11/21/14

Level 2: Collaborative Phase Planning

Phase Planning is the first level of collaborative planning and is used to develop a more detailed work plan that specifies the handoffs between the specialists or trades involved in each phase.

A completed Phase Plan is the design of the project's production system in terms of the work to be done by each crew or craft; and it establishes the conditions for release of work from one group to another. Examples of phases include: Excavation, Foundations, Concrete Pours or Enclosure. Representatives from the professions working within a phase — whether a design or construction phase — collaborate face-to-face when they plan.

More detailed design of specific operations is left for the Production Strategy and Look-Ahead levels, unless details or logistic coordination demand earlier attention.

Building Your Knowledge: Pull Planning

Phase Planning is done using "pull" techniques, i.e., starting at the milestone and working backwards. For each task, the planner is asked, "In order to begin your work, what do you need to have accomplished by the preceding performer?" By focusing on "pull," or a series of requests to the previous performers, the team will be able to define and sequence each task so that its completion releases follow-on work. Following this rule eliminates the waste of overproduction and often eliminates unnecessary work; or causes work to be re-structured in ways that expedite project completion. Moving backwards through the tasks reduces everyone's tendency to simply "do what we have always done" and instead allows teams to begin discussing new methods, negotiate new sequences, and significantly reduce batch size. Chapter 5 includes a section on the "train-themed" daily pull planning tool that subcontractors used.

Level 3: Collaborative Production Strategy and Material Flow

During this phase, the team develops the production rhythm or "takt." In this effort, the team examines a particular phase of the work (for example, installation of overhead systems or production framing and in-wall rough-ins), analyzes the detailed scope and forecasted labor productivity per trade, and develops a strategy that balances production areas and the standard handoff durations or takt times. (The Phase Planning and Production Strategy work may be iterative, where development of one informs the other in cycles of planning.)

Figure 2: The Last Planner System™

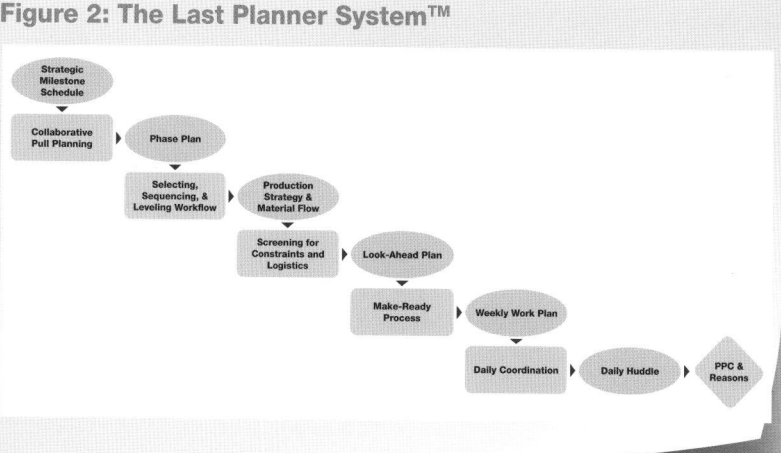

Developing of a successful Production Strategy typically includes the following tasks:

- Soliciting information from the trades concerning optimal crew size, production rates, and preferred path through the physical area.

- Determining optimal trade sequence.

- Dividing each floor or area into sub-areas with similar amounts of work for each trade.

- Assigning disciplines a standard period (e.g., one week, three days, four hours) to complete each sub-area. Only one trade occupies each sub-area at the same time, and each discipline's material is delivered only to its work area.

All disciplines complete and move to the next sub-area at the end of the period, and all progress reporting is aligned and analyzed with completion of each sub-area.

After the overall production strategy is established, it is important to align the supply of material and fabricated components with the demand from the field. All suppliers of material to the project need to be able to support the project demands through a responsive engineering, fabrication, assembly, kitting and delivery process. The supply flow also needs to be designed to ensure accuracy, minimize work-in-process, and be flexible to reduce the exposure to unforeseen design and schedule changes.

Level 4: Look-Ahead Planning and the Constraint Identification and Removal

Look-Ahead Planning (Figure 3) focuses on identifying and ensuring removal of constraints (obstacles that would prevent performance). The size of the look-ahead window (e.g., six weeks) is calibrated to ensure that the team can identify and remove constraints before fabrication or installation of the work is expected to start. Once constraints are identified, the focus turns to securing a Reliable Promise — from an individual, not just a company — for removal of the particular constraint. Again, the focus here is to create high reliability and accountability as a result of public promising. (For a more detailed description of Reliable Promising, see see the Contract section of the Appendix.)

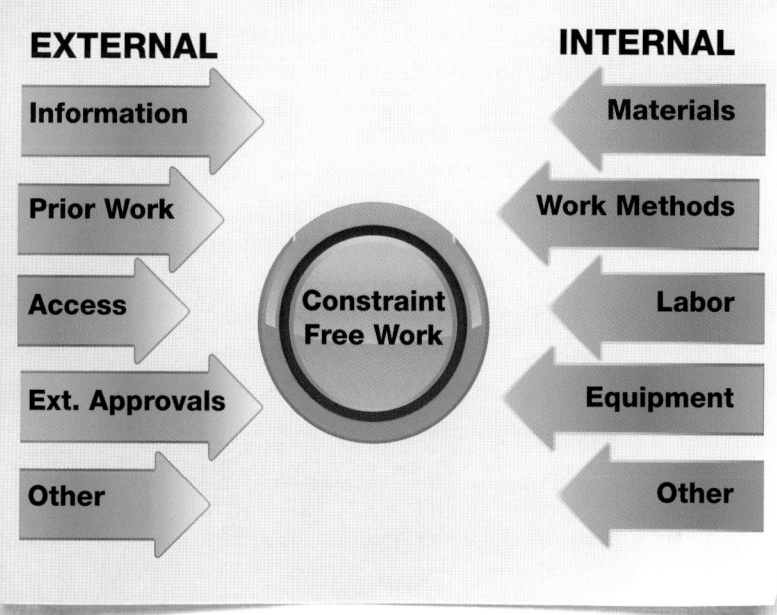

Level 5: Weekly Work Plan Meetings

As the project moves into production, the team begins holding Weekly Work Plan (WWP) Meetings. WWP Meetings focus on ensuring that work is ready for promising; and obtaining and coordinating the promises that will drive the project to completion.

The WWP Meeting looks at the work that should be done according to the Phase Plan; and that can be done as a result of the Look-Ahead Planning Process, and seeks Reliable Promises of what will be done (Weekly Work Plan) during the coming week.

In order to promote Reliable Promises, each Last Planner is asked to review the upcoming week's available work, assure that all constraints have been removed, assess the manpower and other resources he or she will have available during the coming week, and commit only to that work that he or she is confident can be completed during the coming week. Because the Last Planner System is focused on creating workflow reliability, Last Planners should not be encouraged to "over-promise." Rather, they should commit to using 80% to 85% of the labor capacity, building some resilience into the system to account for the uncertainty or variability that frequently creeps in.

In case work proceeds faster than anticipated (or if unanticipated constraints prevent promised work from proceeding), the Last Planner should also identify Workable Backlog. Workable Backlog is future work that also is unconstrained. The team needs to ensure that performing this work early will not harm any other team members.

Level 6: Daily Huddle

The sixth level is the Daily Huddle: a 15-minute stand-up meeting that is held in the field to discuss production from the prior shift and plan for the upcoming shift. It is attended by the Last Planners and typically is facilitated by the field leader for the general contractor. The meeting promotes close-range coordination, focusing on the following questions:

- Any safety issues or concerns last or next shift?

- What did you get done last shift?

- What do you plan to get done next shift?

- Are we still confident in meeting our handoff commitments?

- Is there anything standing in your way (constraint)?

- What deliveries are planned next shift?

- Are there any new topics to be added to our plan?

The focus of the Huddle itself is coordinating action and updating the entire production team on changes or challenges to the plan. If concerns or issues are identified, the team leader should determine whether they could be resolved during the meeting in 30 seconds or less. If not, in order to be efficient with the team's time, the issues should be put in a "parking lot" for a holdover group to address immediately after the Huddle.

Level 7: Review Production Metrics That Compare "Plan" With "Actual"

Each week, the team also reviews the production metrics to identify opportunities for improvement. Each part of the planning system should be reviewed to ensure that it is performing and producing the results expected. If a variance is identified, this presents an opportunity to determine its cause and to improve the process to prevent it from happening again.

The Phase Planning/Look-Ahead processes are designed to ensure that all work is identified in the Look-Ahead Window so it can be scanned for constraints. If work is placed on a WWP or is performed in the field that was not anticipated by the planning system, there is a breakdown in the planning process. The reason for this breakdown should be investigated and the process improved to prevent subsequent failures.

Similarly, if work comes up for promising in the WWP Meeting, but a constraint has not been resolved to release that work, then there has been a failure in the make-ready process. This should be investigated, and the learning should be used to improve the make-ready process.

Finally, each week the team should collect Planned Percent Complete or PPC as a measure of overall workflow reliability. Of the items that individuals committed to completing this week, what percentage of them was actually completed? If they were not done, what was the reason for variance? The team can then investigate the prominent reasons and adopt counter-measures to prevent repeating the same failures.

Engagement, Everywhere, Everyone

Watching From The Windows: Children who were patients at Akron Children's Hospital during the Tower project construction phase curiously watched all of the activity and sometimes joined in. Construction workers performed stretches every day as part of their standard work and soon noticed children in hospital gowns lined up at the windows performing the same stretches. The crews also helped place holiday decorations on the hospital campus, such as this Christmas tree. Patients watched and cheered as the tree was put in place.

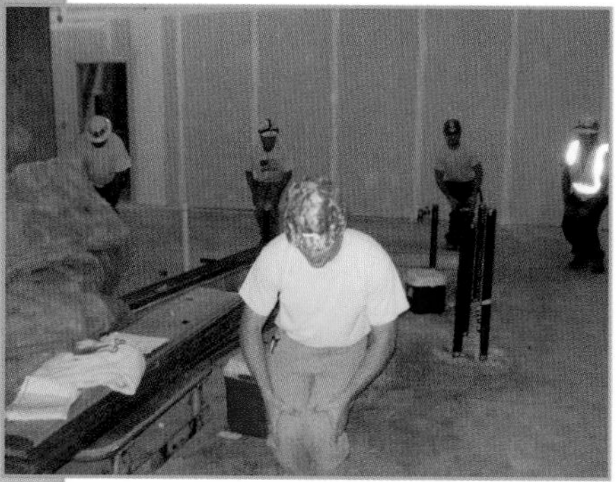

Finance

Address Risk Concerns Through Education

By CFO Mike Trainer and VP/Finance Alicia LaMancusa

Akron Children's used working capital, donations and a municipal bond issue to finance the Tower project. Most of the planning and execution of the funding package was the same as a traditional funding project. However, the Financial team was prepared to answer questions they had anticipated from the rating agencies and other outside groups involved in the financing.

TIPS From The Trenches
Prepare for Skeptics

Don't be surprised to encounter skeptics both inside and outside the organization and be prepared. Education and action can demonstrate the soundness and benefits of IPD to even to the most conservative of financiers.

Rehearse, Rehearse, Rehearse: This is a page from the presentation that the hospital made to the bond-rating agency.

Integrated Project Delivery

Integrated project delivery (IPD) and lean six sigma strategies are being utilized for Master Facility Project construction

Methodology is contractually designed to form a team among the owner, architect and lead contractor. The team collaborates to design and build a structure in a cost effective, high quality, timely manner

Key features of this process include:

- Hired best-in class firms to design and construct the project
- A single Building Information Model (BIM) design and construction platform for use by entire project team
- Measures of Success Scorecard to incentivize "Best-in-Class" performance
- Project Specific Insurance Program – Professional liability, general commercial liability, excess liability, subcontractor default insurance and contractor's pollution liability.
- Pre-established profit and incentive amounts
- Project specific safety program
- Development of Risk Matrix to avoid common errors made
- Owner appointed auditor for project to insure bifurcation of reimbursable costs and profit
- Project mediator/arbitrator pre-selected for speedy dispute resolution
- Big Room collaboration by entire project team
- Warehouse mock-up of floor designs to test the spatial elements of the design

Two Common Concerns About IPD

One likely concern is the nature of IPD vs. traditional project delivery. Another is risk — especially if the owner is borrowing to finance the project. Traditional projects employ a price-lock trigger called a guaranteed maximum price (GMP) as a means of "assigning" the risk of cost overruns. If an owner locks in the GMP early in the project schedule, it pays a higher price but assumes less risk of paying for cost overruns, which tend to rise as the project winds down. If the buyer locks in the GMP closer to the end, it pays less for the project but assumes higher risk of paying cost overruns. IPD does not use GMP.

Also — as is sometimes the case with IPD — the Tower project was replacing existing assets instead of building additional sources of revenue streams. Board members, investors and others might question the value of such a project. This is another opportunity for education. Inefficiency is costly, but it's often defined as a "soft" cost. Not only does IPD itself produce quantifiable cost savings, but its results also do as the resulting work flows are more efficient.

One of the continuous-improvement principles driving IPD is quality-from-the start, which means customers drive design. The outcome is that the resulting product or service provides higher value, i.e., a higher return-on-investment.

Demonstrating The Value Of IPD

Because part of Akron Children's funding was raised through municipal bonds, the hospital had to undergo a credit-rating review. The Financial team understood that they faced a challenge in explaining what could seem like an unnecessarily risky endeavor to the rating professionals. We had to remove doubts about excessive risk in order to earn a rating that would enable borrowing at the interest rate in the financial plan.

The plan worked so well that the CFO — who himself was a skeptic of IPD early on — considers it a successful process. The basic steps we took included:

* Schedule the rating agency (or bank/lender) to visit the organization on site for a presentation and a tour of facilities to be replaced/expanded, if appropriate.

* Include board members, senior executives and other appropriate leaders as part of the presentation. They can answer questions about the project, IPD process and other topics; and their support will add credence to IPD.

* Plan a presentation on the organization's current state (financial health, operations, markets served, forecasted demand, etc.); the future-state plan and the work that produced it; and the role of the IPD process in moving to the future state.

See page 100 more detailed basic steps.

Finally, rehearse, rehearse and rehearse the presentation as well as answers to anticipated questions. It might seem like a small part of the overall project, but when you are assuming debt to fund all or part of the project, how well you can educate outsiders about IPD often will determine how expensive that borrowing is going to be.

Here is more detail on the steps we took:

1. **Develop the financing plan:** To initiate this process, develop a source of use of funds by year for the entire term of the project. Using construction cost estimates by year, the cash flow needs of the project may be arrayed indicating the amount of cash necessary to complete the project. This analysis should forecast the project's impact on the organization's days of cash on hand and strength of the balance sheet.

2. **Determine debt capacity:** Using rating agencies such as Moody's and Fitch, identify *debt-service coverage ratio, debt-to-capitalization ratio and debt-to-cash flow ratio* benchmarks to determine the debt capacity of the organization. The limit on borrowing to support the project can then be determined. Our goal was to strike a level of borrowing of fixed interest municipal bonds that kept us within the sweet spot of the Moody's and Fitch expected benchmark liquidity and debt-capacity ratios to support the desired bond rating.

3. **Plan a financing team:** Select a financing team that believes in the organization's mission and has a willingness to make the financing successful despite encountering challenges on timing, documentation and availability. Our team included: hospital counsel; issuer; issuer counsel; bond counsel; underwriters; underwriter's counsel; hospital auditor; hospital board members; and the rating agency. We found having weekly conference calls to mark progress on the bond issuance to be beneficial.

   a. Request that the rating agencies come for a site visit to see and hear about the organization, its property, the project and the management team.

   b. Benchmark with other bond issue customers the amounts that should be set aside and paid for fees associated with all of the team members. Generally, the underwriter can provide information for benchmarking.

4. **Assess the bond market:** About six weeks prior to the bond issuance, begin to participate with the underwriter in pricing meetings in which bond experts from the underwriter begin to probe interest rates based on recent market conditions and similar-sized offerings. This provides a gauge of interest rates to expect on the day of the bond issuance.

5. **Communicate with Wall Street:** Participate in as many possible interactions with bond buyers and/or buyer conferences as possible. Ask the underwriter to assemble and record a "roadshow" in which the Owner's CEO, CFO and other financial executives, counsel and the underwriter's team present information on the project and the financial health of the organization. Make this recording available to potential buyers prior to the day of the bond sale.

6. **Sell the bonds:** Based on knowledge of the municipal bond market, the underwriter will set the day to price the bonds. Pray for favorable demand and interest rates for that day! At this point, market forces are in charge as the buyers review the bonds, which the underwriter will sell at the most favorable interest rate for the project that is possible based on market forces that day.

CFO MIKE TRAINER: Doubter To Believer

I was dead set against this. Throughout my career projects were constructed with the design, bid, build method. With "design, bid, build" projects, you get the lowest-possible price, and bids sometimes come from five to eight contractors. For each respective trade discipline I thought we were going to accidently overpay for the project with 30% more cost.

I didn't try to stop the enthusiastic embrace of IPD, but I said I had to weigh in. I wanted to make sure on a square-footage basis that this project was reasonably priced. It was 10 months into the project when I saw that figure.

The project was estimated at $260 million, and we chose a $180 million goal. I didn't think we would ever get to $180 million, but bit by bit, the teams moved the needle. When they got to $190 million, I became a believer.

Fundraising

Involve Donors In IPD Opportunities

By John Zoilo, Executive Director of Akron Children's Hospital Foundation

Raising money for capital campaigns is a challenge for any philanthropic organization and has become increasingly difficult as so many corporations, foundations and even individuals prefer giving to programs — i.e., to people — rather than to capital projects. Consequently, fundraisers need to maximize opportunities to engage donors, solicit feedback from prospects, demonstrate fiscal responsibility and, ultimately, turn prospects into financial supporters of not only the project, but also of the organization.

The Integrated Project Delivery (IPD) process provides multiple opportunities to accomplish these goals.

1. Invite Donors To Events

By including donors and prospects in some of the IPD events, an organization can make them feel a part of the entire project with a level of ownership that normally is not afforded to them. And, the more a prospective donor takes ownership of a project, the more likely he/she will give a major gift to ensure that this shared vision is brought to fruition.

TIPS From The Trenches
Include Prospective Donors

Include potential donors in walk-throughs and mock-up sessions, especially if end-users will be participating, too. This gives donors an up-close look at challenges and solutions.

During walk-throughs and mock-up sessions, donors will be able to see design and construction challenges — and solutions — up close. Attending some of these and learning enough of the process to appreciate what's happening can be time-consuming, so make sure the prospective donor has the time.

If donors and prospects can't commit much time, ask them to attend a committee meeting or the "report out" sessions of rapid continuous-improvement events. Even in an abbreviated exposure, the IPD process is a great education vehicle. It also enables donors and prospects to, once again, become part of the process.

2. Demonstrate Value With Hands-On Models

Design sessions that include patients and professionals can physically demonstrate the benefits of the rigorous IPD process. Donors and others (such as members of the public, elected officials, etc.) can experience the design of the new structure before the first shovel of dirt is turned.

We took prospects to the warehouse to observe the design sessions. It was a unique experience for them to learn how this improves delivery of care. They came away impressed.

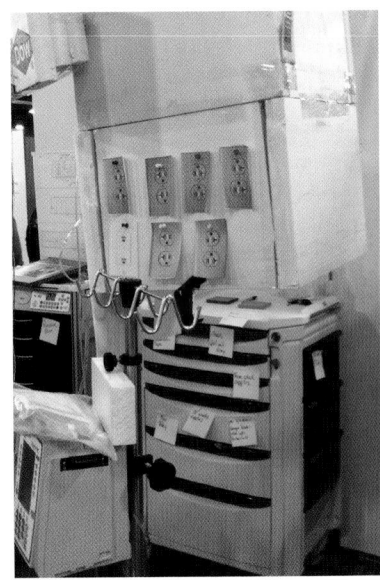

Detailed mock-up at the warehouse.

3. Show Quantifiable Fiscal Responsibility

The entire IPD process reinforces an organization's commitment to fiscal responsibility, something that is obvious in the documented cost and square-footage reductions resulting from rapid continuous-improvement events. The results clearly show donors that their gifts are being used to deliver maximize value to clients.

TIPS From The Trenches
Plan Timing Early

To maximize the benefit of the IPD process, the fundraising team needs to plan for donor/prospect attendance and involvement early. Timing is key as is careful, advanced planning.

Challenges Take Imagination, Planning

In addition to unique advantages, IPD comes with some unique challenges. First, some attributes of the building space are not determined until the entire process is completed. The project's completion date usually is set just a few short weeks/month before the official groundbreaking.

In traditional campaigns, fundraisers secure most of the philanthropic support before the groundbreaking and then the actual building process begins. Consequently, fundraisers must be particularly creative to describe the vision of IPD projects to donors, without the benefit of standard renderings and artist's drawings. This is not an insurmountable hurdle — just be aware that there's not likely to be a host of graphics with which to convince donors to partner with the organization.

We focused on patient benefits of the project, rather than the construction process.

Early on, feedback from select members of our campaign committee — including a former board chair — emphasized that, while the use of IPD represents a creative and new approach, our primary focus and appeal for support should be the improvement in medical care this major capital investment would offer.

We certainly discussed and highlighted the IPD process, but when we did we emphasized how including end users such as patients and patient families along with doctors, nurses and clinicians will make for a much more efficient and operationally functioning building.

Another challenge is that fundraisers should not over-emphasize IPD: It's a tool, not the entire toolbox. While donors are concerned with fiscal responsibility, the large, major philanthropists are giving because they "believe" in the cause and want to help. They might enjoy hearing about the IPD process, but it's not the determining factor for donation.

Finally, the IPD process is just that — a process. It ends. Fundraisers need to act quickly to capitalize on the three opportunities detailed previously. These activities pass by quickly, and donors can be busy people.

The IPD process can help with any fundraising effort if used appropriately. This unique design and construction model can help to generate philanthropic dollars for not-for-profit organizations with capital needs, as long as there's early planning to address the challenges.

 # Engagement, Everywhere, Everyone

Lego™ Building Project: Originally planned as a fundraising project, an event inviting prospective donors to use Lego™ blocks to "build" the hospital quickly attracted many more participants.

The Graffiti Project: Another fundraising event invited former hospital patients to "tag" the foundational structure of the Tower with their names so that they would always remain a part of Akron Children's Hospital.

Kay Jewelers

The relationship between Akron Children's Hospital and Signet Jewelers Ltd. goes back many years. Signet is the largest specialty retail jewelry company in the US, UK and Canada, and has been headquartered in Akron for more than 100 years. Its US Sterling Division store brands today include Kay Jewelers® and Jared® the Galleria of Jewelry. Sterling has long been a corporate supporter for the hospital including a major gift in 2007 to create the Sterling Respite Area within the Hospital's Reinberger Family Center.

In 2003 Robert D. Trabucco, Sterling's Chief Financial Officer, joined the Akron Children's Foundation Board and became a volunteer at the hospital. Beginning in 2006 Bob took on the responsibility for chairing the Foundation's Annual Fund Appeal. In the intervening years, Sterling's involvement with Hospital activities deepened and as Bob was elected to the Children's hospital board in 2009 and currently serves as Chairman of the Board. Another company executive, David Bouffard, Signet VP of Corporate Affairs, was elected to the Foundation board in 2009 and today chairs the Foundation Board's Marketing Committee and participates on the Foundation's Corporate Alliance Task Force.

With David championing the effort, in 2012, Sterling made another important gift to establish a Division of Corporate Alliances within the Foundation. The challenge to embrace the idea of Corporate Alliances, with programs including cause-related marketing, as a long-term strategy arose from the success Sterling had partnering nationally with another children's hospital. Sterling has continued to increase its support of the hospital with several programs engaging employee involvement under the leadership of Jody Wolf, Signet's Vice President, Business Support Services. The company has chosen Akron Children's Hospital to be its primary charity of choice in its headquartered market.

As the Building-on-the-Promise capital campaign got underway, Sterling was one of the top prospects identified for a leadership gift to the campaign. As conversations continued with Sterling around a significant level of support for the new Medical Care Tower began it soon became apparent that given the expanding relationship between Sterling and Children's created the opportunity to discuss participation in the Promise Campaign at a much higher level of support, specifically a gift that would provide the opportunity to name the new building and in 2014, the pacesetting gift request was approved by the Signet Board of Directors. In recognition of that outstanding generosity, the new medical care building will be named the Kay Jewelers Pavilion.

Communications

Past And Future Connect Online

By Holly Pupino, Media Relations Specialist, Akron Children's Hospital

For Akron Children's Communications team, the most important story to tell about the Tower project was it's connection to a promise made in 1890 when the hospital opened: To care for all children who came through the doors, regardless of a family's ability to pay. The "Building on the Promise" campaign also linked the hospital's 125th anniversary in 2015 to the Tower opening.

Integrated Project Delivery (IPD) was part of that larger story and also set the project apart and aligned with existing key messages, such as a commitment to family-centered care, lean/Six Sigma operations, and being a good steward of financial resources. Along with providing these advantages, the IPD component also needed to be explained and articulated in the messaging.

The Tower project itself was a complex and fast-moving program with multiple audiences. The Communications team identified these practices as keys to success:

- **Using a dedicated website.** Launched in April 2013, building. akronchildrens.org serves as a repository for all facets of the building project, and features the latest news, blog posts, photos, videos and frequently asked questions.

- **Use the IPD angle to promote articles:** Share it with local media, hospital trade media and building industry media. It is interesting and compelling.

We used a website dedicated to the Tower project as a launch pad for multiple communication formats. Some are described here.

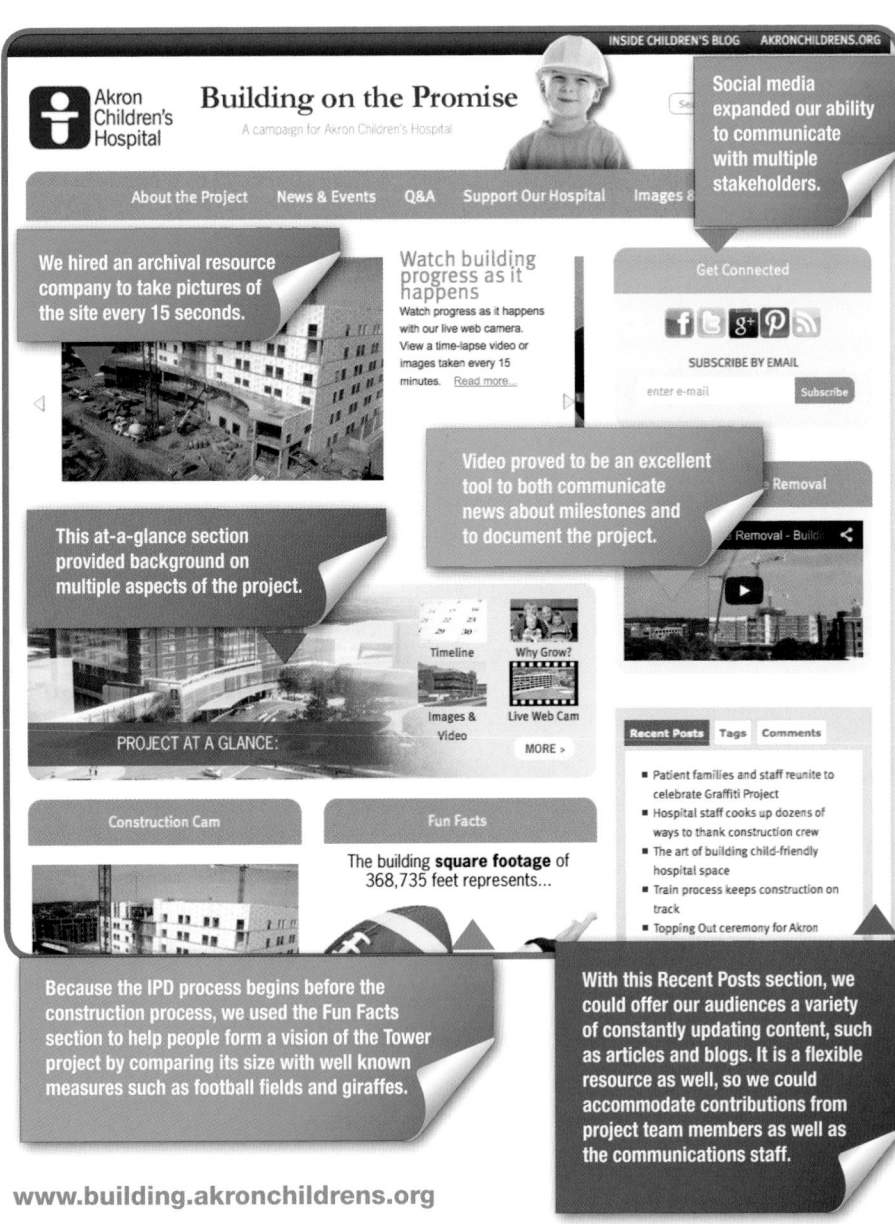

Social media expanded our ability to communicate with multiple stakeholders.

We hired an archival resource company to take pictures of the site every 15 seconds.

Video proved to be an excellent tool to both communicate news about milestones and to document the project.

This at-a-glance section provided background on multiple aspects of the project.

Because the IPD process begins before the construction process, we used the Fun Facts section to help people form a vision of the Tower project by comparing its size with well known measures such as football fields and giraffes.

With this Recent Posts section, we could offer our audiences a variety of constantly updating content, such as articles and blogs. It is a flexible resource as well, so we could accommodate contributions from project team members as well as the communications staff.

www.building.akronchildrens.org

- **Use video:** Visually document the process and the changing look of the hospital campus for the historic record and also to use in the campaign.

- **Use social media:** Human-interest stories related to the project work well.

TIPS From The Trenches:
Make a Video Archive

The Communications team contracted with EarthCam, an archival resource that took photos of the construction site every 15 minutes. Each week, the photos were compiled into a time-lapsed video of construction progress to date.

Another key was staying in contact with the project. The Communications team relied on regular meetings of a cross-functional team for this.

The communications steering committee included administrators, project managers and architects, clinicians involved in design, the hospital's PR/marketing leadership, as well as specialists in internal/employee communications, media relations, and Foundation (fundraising) communications.

Information from the monthly meetings fed into updates — particularly aimed at potential donors — and media coverage. More importantly, they gave the Communications team the opportunity to learn of good stories to share.

Website Content, Design

The site was colorful and engaging. A "Fun Facts" section compared the height of the new building to 11 giraffes and the square footage to six Goodyear blimps, six football fields or 27 Olympic-size swimming pools.

Other content included:

- **Stories and videos that focused on the IPD process**
  Example: A kaizen during which ER doctors and nurses spent several days in a local warehouse planning their new space and even staging a mock trauma to be sure they had doorways wide enough for stretchers.

- **Features on the participants**
  Example: A story on the project superintendent and his life-long love of the construction industry.

- **Stories that document milestones**
  Example: The groundbreaking and topping-out ceremonies.

- **Stories that harken back to the hospital's mission**

  Example: A story on the "graffiti project" that showed how the names of patients nominated by staff members were spray-painted on structural beams in the new building — eventually to be covered by the exterior façade and yet always there.

Several blog posts were written by participants in the IPD process, including parents who brought their hospital experiences to the design process, an ENT specialist who shared his ideas on how to make outpatient surgery the best experience it could be, and a pediatrician/Operations Excellence expert who wrote about the challenge of designing a new medical building in the midst of healthcare reform when the future of hospitals is very uncertain.

As a practical matter, the blog was also a good place to direct colleagues from other hospitals; contractors and suppliers associated with the project; external professionals who wanted to learn, and media who needed to check facts, get access to photos and videos, and keep abreast of the latest developments.

TIPS from the Trenches:
Share Among The Team

Share the story of your unique building process with a supplier's employee newsletter. Be open to media pitches from the PR firm representing the general contractor. But be sure everyone is on the same page and credit is given where credit is due.

Moving forward, the communication team's challenge will be internal. As the opening date of the new building moves closer, furniture, equipment, and most importantly patients — particularly fragile neonates — will move into the new building. The challenge will be to communicate numerous details, new phone numbers, moving dates, and way-finding instructions for patient families in a timely manner.

While different communication tactics are needed for various audiences, the success of the "Building on the Promise" campaign came down to people and stories.

Bricks and mortar don't generate emotional ties, but children do, and so the doctors and nurses committed to caring for them.

Appendix

Legal and Technical Information

Part 1: Contract Basics

I.   Integrated Agreement For Lean Project Delivery
II. Contract Language: A Focus On Cooperation And Collaboration
III. Reliable Promising: Crucial For Success
IV. Joining Agreement: A Commitment To The Team
V.   The Decision-Makers: Project Leadership Team

Part 2: Risk And Reward

I.   Establishing Total Project Cost (Target Cost)
II. Incentive Compensation
III. Measuring Success: Quality Control And Motivation

Part 3: Insurance

I.   Project-specific Insurance
II. The Insurance Partner Solution
III. Choosing An Underwriter
IV. Administrating Owner-Controlled Insurance
V.   Lessons Learned

Part 4: Documents and Graphics

I.   NICU, Outpatient Surgery and Emergency Department teams
II. Master Project Dashboard
III. A3: Prefab NICU Bathroom Construction Method
IV. A3: NICU Headwall Study
V.   PLT Dashboard (partial view)

I. Integrated Agreement For Lean Project Delivery

A non-traditional project-delivery method requires a non-traditional contract to define the participating parties' roles.

In a traditional design-and-construct project, the Owner oftentimes contracts directly and separately with an architect for design and with a contractor or construction manager for construction. These contracts clearly define the scope of work and the roles and responsibilities of each party. The scope, however, is limited to the predefined piece of the project each party is responsible for completing. If the project requires work outside of the defined scope, the parties address it through a change order: price gets adjusted, scope gets adjusted, and the change ripples through the multiple contracts.

There's an effort to establish responsibilities and accountability between the Owner and each of the contracted parties — but not among the contracted parties. Any miscommunication or lack of communication among the contracted party is the Owner's problem.

The IPD contract Akron Children's (the Owner) developed for the Tower Project (the Project) intentionally included all of the key participants in the contract either as a direct signatory to the Integrated Agreement for Lean Project Delivery (IALPD) or by way of a Joining Agreement that included the design consultants and trade partners identified and selected by the integrated project delivery team (IPD Team) and brought onto the project team. In Akron Children's case, the IALPD was a five-party agreement executed by the Owner, the local architect, the national architect, the local construction manager and the national construction manager.

All five members of the IPD Team expressed great expectations and enthusiasm at the contract-signing luncheon, but this came only after a great deal of collaborative thought and dialogue.

Since the Owner, local architect and local construction manager had no experience with IPD, and the national architect had moderate experience at this delivery method, representatives from the five teams met for three days to discuss:

- The IPD method;
- Project goals for each of the five parties; and,
- Parameters and expectations to be set forth in the contract.

TIPS from the Trenches:
Establish Ground Rules

Getting everyone on the same page from the beginning is a "must do" and makes the contract drafting and negotiations much easier because the ground rules have been established.

A person well versed in the IPD method facilitated the meeting by walking team members through the concepts, definitions and pitfalls associated with IPD.

Building a strong team, sharing risk as a team, and sharing in the rewards that a successful team effort would generate resonated throughout the three days, and the discussion and resulting ideas laid the foundation for the contract. It was also agreed that all decisions would be made based on what was in the best interest of the Project and not the individual team members.

II. Contract Language:
A Focus On Collaboration And Cooperation

The Owner took responsibility for generating the first draft of the agreement, but the contract language didn't define individual rights and responsibilities or duties and obligations. Rather, it focused on the Project, collaboration, Reliable Promising and the advantages of an IPD Team pursuing the project initiatives:

> "By forming an IPD Team, the Parties intend to gain the benefit of an open and creative learning environment, where team members are encouraged to share ideas freely in an atmosphere of mutual respect and tolerance. Team members shall work together and individually to achieve a transparent and cooperative exchange of information in all matters relating to the Project and to share ideas for improving Project delivery to achieve the maximum number of Owner desired components identified on The Projects Objectives. Team members shall actively promote harmony, collaboration and cooperation among all entities performing on the Project." (IALPD Section 3.3)

It's important to reiterate that an IALPD requires as a material term of the contract that the parties "collaborate" as a team. Note also that except for a few limited reservations, the Owner accepts the fact that it's just another member of the team agreeing to collaborate in accordance with the rules set forth by the team.

III. Reliable Promising: Crucial For Success

For the team approach to work, there has to be a requirement that once a promise to the team is made, the promisor performs the required task according to the parameters set by the team so the rest of the team can move forward relying on that promise.

The IPD team considered this concept of Reliable Promising to be crucial for success, so members made it a contract requirement. The team posted the tenets of Reliable Promising (listed below) on the walls of the Big Room, where the design process took place; and Mission Control, where the construction process was managed.

- The conditions of satisfaction are clear to both parties — the promisor and the IPD team.

- The promisor is competent to perform the task; or has access to the competence to perform the task; or has access to the competence to perform the task and the wherewithal (materials, tools, equipment, instructions).

- The promisor has estimated the time to perform the task and has internally allocated adequate resources and has blocked the time on her, his or its internal schedule.

- The promisor is sincere in the moment that the promise is made — there is no current basis for believing that the promise cannot or will not be fulfilled.

- The performer/promisor is prepared to accept the legal and reasonable consequences that may ensue if the promise cannot be performed as promised and will promptly advise the Project Leadership Team and IPD Team if confidence is lost that the task can be performed as promised.

IV: Joining Agreement: A Commitment To The Team

The design consultants and trade partners selected by the PLT after the IALPD has been signed come on board by signing a Joining Agreement. The Joining Agreement is a simple three-page document requiring that each signing party:

- Comply with the terms and conditions of the IALPD;

- Participate fully in all IPD Team functions and Big Room collaboration; and,

- Use the BIM (building information model) platform selected for the Project.

The Joining Agreement also reiterates the principles of Reliable Promising, taking the opportunity to again state the importance of being a committed team player.

V. The Decision-Makers:
Project Leadership Team

Instead of having all the Project decisions run by the Owner for approval (as is common in a traditional contract), the contract provides that leadership resides in the Project Leadership Team (PLT). Seven members comprised Akron Children's PLT.

Each of the architects and construction management firms appointed a representative. The Owner appointed two representatives along with a representative of the Owner's Representative. Note, however, that the Owner's right to appoint two representatives and have its Owner's Representative on the PLT is not to stack the voting in favor of the Owner. Rather, it is the Owner's desire to have its Director of Engineering and VP of Facilities involved in the Project. The Owner's Representative's involvement is a function of engaging the person in the collaboration and conversation because the Owner is paying for him to be part of the Project. Control actually rests with all of the members of the PLT because all decisions made by the PLT must be unanimous.

> *"The PLT will manage and coordinate implementation of the Project Objective and provide leadership and direction to the IPD Team and the Project Implementation Teams... PLT decisions are final and not subject to review or modification except by a subsequent PLT action or an Owner's Directive.... Each Party will assure that its PLT representatives, or designated alternates, attend all PLT meetings, have authority to act on behalf of the Party, and fulfill his or her responsibilities as PLT members." (Excerpts from Section 4.1 of the IALPD)*

This horizontal decision-making structure, a radical departure from traditional vertical decision-making, is what makes IPD work. The "buck" stops with the PLT in nearly every case.

I. Establishing Total Project Cost (Target Cost)

A distinguishing difference between traditional contracting methods and an IPD contract is the sharing of risks and rewards by all IPD Team members. The IALPD spells out how risks and rewards will be allocated to each member.

The IPD Team — and more importantly the PLT — establishes the total project costs (Target Cost, see Figure 1), which is made up of three components:

1. **Reimbursable Costs**

2. **Contingency**

3. **Profit**

Reimbursable Costs

The Owner agrees to pay for all Reimbursable Costs incurred on the Project by the IPD Team. Reimbursable Costs are defined in the IALPD as those cost categories that include the architects and design consultants; contractor and trade partners; and Owner costs incurred in the performance of the work (time and materials costs) excluding any contingency and profit.

Exhibits to the IALPD detail what costs can be recovered in hourly rates being charged to the Project and in materials being purchased for the Project. The Owner is essentially guaranteeing payment of time and materials committed to and placed in the Project regardless of whether the total Project costs comes in at, under or over the Target Cost.

Contingency

The Project contingency is a defined amount to be used by all of the IPD Team including the Owner. The fund is intended to cover costs for:

• Project elements not known when Target Cost is set;

• Errors and omissions;

• Increases in materials prices and labor rates;

• Deductibles for insured losses; and,

• Warranty work.

A benefit of the IPD method is that all the layers of contingency funds that get priced into a traditional multi-tiered construction project are scrubbed out of all of the contracts and pooled in the allocated contingency fund for use if needed by anyone on the IPD Team.

In a traditional contract arrangement, each contracting party at each tier of contracting keeps its unspent contingency at the end of the contract. Those unspent dollars do nothing to benefit the Project or the Project participants. In the IALPD, these unspent contingency funds can be used to put additional "want" items into the Project and/or be distributed to the IPD Team as part of the incentive-payment plan.

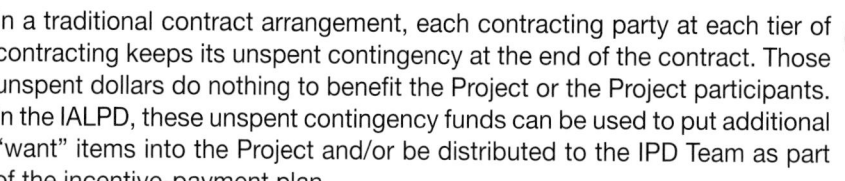

Profit

As with contingency, the IALPD and the IPD method expects profit at all tiered levels of contracting to be identified at the commencement of the Project and included in a "profit bucket."

These dollars are put at risk by the IPD Team. Just as the Owner has agreed to the risk of having to pay for all Reimbursable Costs to complete the Project even if such costs exceed the Target Cost, the IPD Team agrees to put all of its profit at risk if the Reimbursable Costs exceed the expected amount after spending all of the designated contingency funds.

The IPD method is based on driving out costs associated with waste, rework, redesign and inefficient processes. Because the IPD Team believes this will occur as a result of pursuing the IPD method, profit is identified and fixed at the beginning of the Project for two reasons. First, it is a necessary evil to establish the Target Cost. Second, it fixes the expected profit of each IPD Team member early so as not to penalize the team for driving costs out of the Project budget. To put it another way, team participants are not conflicted with final profit being tied to a percentage of final design costs. Reducing costs through design innovation, process improvement and better planning provides more funds for the other Project needs and wants without reducing the IPD Team's expected reward.

Figure 1: Target Cost Example

Target Cost: $180,000,000
Reimbursable Costs (approximated) = $160,000,000
Contingency pool = $10,000,000
Profit (at risk) = $10,000,000

TIPS from the Trenches:

3 Factors To Consider For Profit Allocation

Establishing profit allocation is one of the early challenges and serves as an early indicator about how well the team will work together. This task is made easier when you consider three factors.

1. The selection process the Owner goes through to identify the initial IPD Team should produce mutual trust, and therefore, an open willingness to be fair from the perspectives of the Owner and other project participants.

2. There are industry benchmarks for establishing reasonable profit levels for comparably sized projects and firms.

3. With IPD being such a new delivery method, there is an intangible reward for the participants to be part of the Project and, therefore, perhaps more willing to place more emphasis on the overall incentive program of the Project than on the Profit component.

II. Profit And Incentive:

The IALPD Profit and Incentive Compensation Plan is made up of four components:

1. Profit-at-Risk

2. Incentive Compensation (IC)

3. Allocation of Project Savings

4. Payout based on the Measures of Success Scorecard

Profit-at-Risk

Ninety percent of each IPD Team members' expected profit — which has been previously fixed and approved by the PLT — is funded by Target Cost dollars and set aside as Profit-at-Risk. The other 10% of the expected profit funds (Target Cost dollars) are set aside as Incentive Compensation (IC), explained in the next section.

If total Project costs come in at Target Cost, then each IPD Team member will be paid its entire Profit-at-Risk component (that is, 90% of its expected profit) and its other 10% of expected profit allocated to the IC plan to the extent earned in accordance with the Measures of Success Scorecard (see Figure 2).

Incentive Compensation (IC)

IC is funded in three ways:

- 10% allocation of each IPD Team members' expected profit;
- Project Savings resulting from less-than-expected Reimbursable Costs actually paid out by Owner (see Figure 3); and,
- Contingency funds not used on the Project.

TIPS from the Trenches:

Don't Underestimate Early Savings

The allocation of Project savings is intended to be shared by the entire IPD Team, which includes the Owner. In Akron Children's case, the Owner proposed splitting evenly the first $2 million of the savings because they considered these savings to be low-hanging fruit. In retrospect, there was more low-hanging fruit that should have been divided equally. The first few million in project savings is relatively easy to achieve in an IPD project. (Note though, that the Owner's allocation of the savings can be used for whatever purpose the Owner elects.)

Allocation of Project Savings

In Akron Children's contract, the parties agreed that the Project Savings be allocated as follows:

Figure 2: Allocation of Project Savings

Amount of Savings	Incentive Compensation	Owner
Up to $2,000,000	50%	50%
From $2,000,001 to total Potential Reward for all IC Plan Participants	100%	0%
Additional Savings above the total Potential Reward for all ICL Participants	10%	90%

The Potential Reward is defined as the total profit to be paid on the Project multiplied by a factor of 1.5. Hence, under the IC Plan, each ICL Team Member has the potential of earning up to 50% or more of its expected profit fixed at the beginning of the project. The third layer of Savings was added so as not to dis-incentivize the team in the event the second tier is fully funded. (Note, however, that since the IPD Team has fully funded 150% of its total potential reward in the second layer, if Savings are realized at this third tier, then the benefits of the IPD method may be working against the Owner since — under the IPD model — the Project savings after funding the potential reward should be going back into the Project cost as an added benefit to the Owner's final Project.)

Measures of Success Scorecard

If the actual Project costs are less than the Target Cost, the IPD Team members will receive their total Profit-at-Risk component. The IC component, however, is earned by satisfying the Measures of Success developed by the PLT and approved as part of the IC plan. The Measure of Success Scorecard is based on a possible 100 earnable points. The points are converted to a percentage score, which is then multiplied by the total IC amount available for distribution to each IPD Team member.

Several examples of how the Profit and Incentive Compensation Plan may work based on actual Project Cost versus Target Cost are provided in Figures 3–5.

Figure 3: Total Project Cost Equals Target Cost

Target Cost $180,000,000

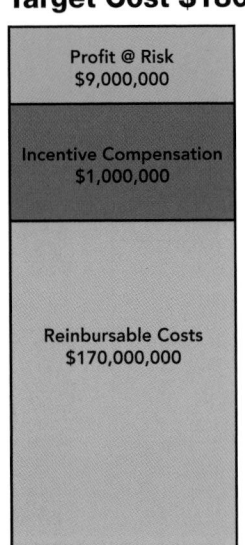

Scenario 1: Total Project Costs equal Target Cost

Incentive Compensation
Up to $1,000,000 — 50/50
$500,000 to Owner
$500,000 to Team to get entire 500k - Team must score 100%
Measures of Success

Figure 4: Total Project Cost Equals $163,000,000

Target Cost $180,000,000

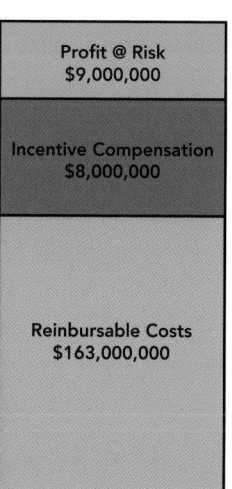

Scenario 2: Total Project Costs equals $172,000,000

Incentive Compensation
Up to $2,000,000
• ACH 50% - $1,000,000
• Team 50% - $1,000,000

$2,000,000 to $7,000,000
• $5,000,000 to Team

Above $7,000,000
• ACH 90%
• Team 10%

Figure 5: Actual Cost Exceeds Target Cost

Scenario 3: Actual Cost Exceeds Target Cost

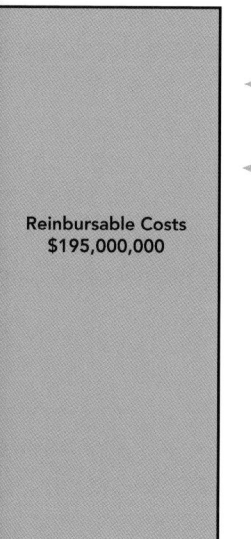

⬅ Actual Cost $195,000,000

Target Cost $180,000,000
⬅

Profit
Incentive
Compensation

-0-

• Owner Pays all Reimbursable Costs
• No Profit-at-Risk Paid
  • ICL Participants return any Milestone Profit
  • Distributions paid out by owner
• No Incentive Compensation Paid

III. Measuring Success:
Quality Control And Motivation

Establishing the Measures of Success proved to be one of the more difficult tasks in completing the IALPD. The PLT was tasked with developing the descriptors defining a successful Project for all involved going back to the initial three-day discussions as well as the earlier selection process for the initial five-member IPD Team. Even more challenging was establishing the quantitative measures to determine success in each category. The measures needed to be a stretch to insure the Owner received the high-quality Project it expected but also be achievable to serve as an incentive to the IPD team.

TIPS from the Trenches:

Quantitative And Qualitative Measures

The Measures of Success need to be both quantitative and qualitative. The "soft" measures need to be included in the scoring process because the true success of an IPD Project is not entirely quantifiable.

The risk-reward structure needs to reach down to the people who actually do the work. The business entities making up the IPD Team received standard payment but the plan also required that at least 10% of the incentive compensation be distributed to those employees who worked on the Project above and beyond what an employee's regular annual bonus might be. (Note, employee bonuses shown to be a regular component of the company's compensation structure was an allowable cost under the definition of Reimbursable Costs.)

Additional reward programs were also implemented by the PLT and budgeted for in the Target Cost. Don't underestimate the importance of including the boots on the ground workers in the incentive plan to encourage teamwork and Project success.

The Measures of Success selected by the PLT are set forth in Figure 6. They reflect what the Owner expected to achieve from the Project as well as the other IPD Team members involved.

Figure 6: Project Success Metrics

SUCCESS MATRIX COMPONENTS

- Safety
- Local participation
- Energy efficiency
- Team performance
- Scheduled
- Quality
- LEED
- Staff and family satisfaction

Warranty

The cost of post-Project warranty work is factored into the Contingency component of the Target Cost and is intended to be held back by the Owner until the warranty period expires. It took the attorneys involved a while to get the warranty provision right. The final warranty language was set out in the First Amendment to the IALPD along with the final insurance program.

Working through the warranty "what ifs" was challenging because of the insurance underwriter's unwillingness — understandable unwillingness — to insure the correction of defective work that constituted warranty-related work. Another complicating factor was getting buy-in from the IPD Team that potential warranty work could consume all of each team member's incentive compensation and profit earned and paid. The warranty language provides an Owner's right to "claw back" first incentive compensation then profit paid to the team members to cover the cost of the warranty repair work. To the extent the warranty reserve funds are not spent by the Owner for approved warranty work at the end of the warranty period, the remaining funds are distributed to the IPD Team as part of and in accordance with the Incentive Compensation Plan.

Although there was a great deal of discussion regarding who pays the deductible and who benefits from the insurance program, the IPD Team agreed that the cost of the insurance and the deductibles, if any, incurred would be a Project cost and be included in the Target Cost. As discussed in Part 3 addressing the insurance programs, the insurance was put into place for the benefit of the entire team for a number of valid reasons. Therefore, the entire team would contribute to any deductible incurred by the Owner after the Project is completed but in this case, only to the extent an IPD Team Member has received an Incentive Compensation component payment.

PART 3: INSURANCE

Compiled By Tim Ziga, Associate General Counsel Akron Children's Hospital

I. Project-Specific Insurance

The resources we studied on Integrated Project Delivery (IPD) encouraged buying project-specific insurance for all the reasons to be noted in this chapter. However, when we investigated actual IPD projects, we learned that very few, if any, went that route. Most relied on traditional methods for insuring the project.

Akron Children's Hospital chose to go with a project-specific insurance package prepared by a local insurance brokerage company because it better supported the IPD principles and provided the opportunity to use partners with what turned out to be valuable expertise and skills.

Building Your Knowledge

Insurance Coverage: Important Questions

Common insurance coverage secured for a design-and-construct project includes: Builder's Risk, Commercial General Liability ("GCL"), Worker's Compensation, Pollution Liability, Subcontractor Default and Professional Design. They all cover different aspects of the project and different parties working on the project.

Understanding that each participant has its own coverage extended by its own insurance program, there are a number of questions an Owner needs to ask and document.

- Who is the first named insured and who are named additional insureds on the policy?
- Is the Owner a named additional insured?
- What are the types and limits of coverage being provided by a project participant?
- What coverage is excluded from a participant's insurance policy?
- What is the term of policy coverage?
- Does the policy expire during the project?
- Are the policies claims-made or occurrence-based programs?
- Is the policy an excess coverage program?
- Is there an umbrella policy to secure higher limits?
- Who must make the claim?
- Do defense costs erode the limits of coverage ultimately available to the Owner of the project?

Challenges With IPD Project Insurance

Traditionally, an Owner secures the Builder's Risk policy insuring the project work. The Owner then looks to the contractor and subcontractors to provide commercial general liability and subcontractor default coverage; and the architect and design consultants to provide professional liability insurance in addition to commercial general liability coverage. The Owner or contractor can provide pollution-liability coverage.

1. Contractor/Subcontractor Coverage

Project participants at each tier must secure designated, redundant coverage, and they pass the cost through. Oftentimes, the coverage limits and types of coverage they retain are too low in relation to the risk and liability associated with a large design-and-construct project. In some cases, the lower-tier subcontractors and design team members (smaller local trades and professionals) simply can't get the coverage an Owner requires to cover the risk and liability, and so are excluded from participating.

TIPS From The Trenches:
Carefully Consider Requirements Vs. Cost

In addition to the premium, insurance deductibles add to project cost at every level. The Owner could require a deductible that is lower than what a subcontractor's standard policy provides, but this also would add cost to the project because the subcontractor will have to buy additional coverage to meet the requirement. The same happens if the Owner requires expanded coverage types or removal of certain exclusions. Repeating this with every contractor can add significant pass-through costs that don't translate into a better outcome for the project.

2. Fault and Gaps

With multiple participants maintaining multiple insurance plans, the question of fault looms large when an insurable incident occurs. For the Owner trying to get a project completed, the process of determining fault — or in some cases comparative fault — can become a huge distraction to the project. Couple that with determining fault by taking into consideration policy exclusions, deductibles or limits, and there may be a gap in coverage.

Requiring reasonable limits of liability from the project participants does not guarantee coverage. The actual dollars available to make a claim could be limited by the dollars already paid out on other claims the contractor/subcontractor may have incurred within the applicable policy year including — possibly — defense costs paid or to be paid on one or more claim(s).

If one of the project participants has a bad claims year, a project may not have the coverage the Owner expects. The solution may be for the Owner to incur additional project costs by securing coverage to plug possible gaps.

3. Fear of Collaboration

Finally, policy requirements in the individual policies each participant brings to the project can impede collaboration, which IPD requires. No one will want to venture outside a company's sphere of expertise for fear of creating or falling under an exclusion of coverage on a potential claim. This minefield of exclusions and coverage limits became clearly evident during our discussions with potential underwriters.

To address these challenges, we elected to pursue securing a project-specific insurance program. If everyone would be expected to participate equally in the design and development of the project, we needed a protection plan that also encouraged true innovation in an IPD environment.

TIPS From The Trenches:
Identifying An Insurance Broker

We set out to identify an insurance broker that had:

- experience with unconventional insurance packages;
- expertise in handling the combination of different types of coverage; and,
- the ability to be readily accessible for counseling and claims management if needed.

We were fortunate to have identified The Oswald Companies, a group of highly skilled professionals living in the communities the hospital serves. As we began putting the design program together, we discovered that our broker insured nearly 80% of the local and national firms participating in the project.

II. The Insurance Partner Solution

Our insurance partner helped us create a project-specific insurance program that included the builder's risk coverage, commercial general liability coverage, Owner's pollution-liability coverage, worker's compensation coverage through the hospital, and professional liability coverage for the entire contract term and project team.

Oswald Companies' support included helping to price different limits of coverage and ultimately determine the limits reasonable for a project of our size. Subcontractor default coverage was put in place through the contractor's subcontractor default program with Oswald's analytical support.

Even with our partner's help, putting this type of program into place was no easy task. I soon learned why most IPD projects defaulted to the traditional insurance method. Basically, the insurance underwriters don't quite get IPD yet and, therefore, make it very difficult to structure an IPD-specific insurance plan the meets the needs of the project.

The IALPD (see Appendix, Part 1: Contract Basics) is essentially a no-fault contract. Except for a handful of claims scenarios arising out of fraud or non-payment, the IPD Team members waive claims and associated liability each may have against the others in order to maximize collaboration and teamwork.

This approach made traditional underwriters uncomfortable because it removes finger pointing and the blame game. Instead, if a problem arises during the project, the IPD Team takes on the task of finding a fix within the Project's Target Cost. Combining the traditional Owner-controlled insurance program components with the professional liability coverage component also was an over-the-top concept for underwriters.

The fact the Akron Children's was willing to waive all other claims against the team enhanced both collaboration and creativity in design and construction but also eased transactions with our insurer as more than 65% of all claims arise from the Owner. Thus, we were insuring only the other 35% plus any third-party liability; as well as any rectifying situation we discovered while designing the project.

Having an experienced insurance partner on the team helped immensely with selecting an underwriter that also was willing to think outside-the-box and become a member of our IPD Team.

Benefits of Project-Specific Insurance

- The insurance program supports the IPD philosophy and provides the IPD Team with an insurance platform that encourages collaboration and cross-disciplinary, innovative decision-making.

- The Owner can select the types of coverage it wants for the project.

- The Owner can establish the limits of liability for each type of insurance coverage selected based upon the Owner's appetite for risk and the size of the project.

- The Owner is the first insured on the policies along with all of the other IPD Team members and (in most cases) project participants electing to meet the insurance program enrollment requirements.

- The Owner can establish what endorsements are needed for the project and what exclusions are appropriate and make sense for the project.

- The Owner can fix the term of the policy and negotiate any extended-claims reporting period required to address concerns for future claim liability.

- The insurance program's limits of liability are specific to the Owner's project and cannot be eroded by other projects.

- The Owner can establish excess coverage that makes sense for the project and layer the coverage in a manner to control premium costs.

- The Owner can establish the amount of self-insured retention or deductible to be set for each of the components of the insurance program based on what makes sense for the Project.

In our case, the IPD Team weighed in on what the limits of liability should be and how much self-insured risk the team should take. Since the decision was made to make the insurance cost part of the IALPD Target Cost (in lieu of the Owner securing project insurance on its own), the IPD Team participated in discussions to determine what were reasonable limits based upon insurance premium price points. The Owner made the final decisions because the Owner was the sponsor of the insurance program.

Alternate Insurance Options

CCIP: Another way for an IPD project to obtain a project-specific insurance program is to stipulate that the contractor provide the insurance program, at least as it pertains to commercial general liability, employer liability, subcontractor default and project-pollution coverage through a contractor controlled insurance program (CCIP).

The professional liability component of the program — while a separate policy — was with the same carrier to assure coverage disputes would be minimized; i.e., merely deciding if it was a general liability issue or a professional liability one.

IPIP: The IPD contract can specify who is to provide what project insurance and what the limits of liability and self-insured retention (deductible) limits will be. There may be some forward-thinking underwriters that will combine the professional liability piece with the traditional CCIP. For example, the Boldt Company, the Tower project's general contractor, is working with one underwriter to try to create an Integrated Project Insurance Program (IPIP) product for the marketplace to allow the contractor to step into the shoes of the Owner and provide the project-specific insurance program as part of its services to the Owner.

Existing Insurance: The hospital's existing insurance program offered two opportunities to cover some of the liability exposure for this project. The hospital has its own self-insured worker's compensation program with the State of Ohio's Worker's Compensation Bureau (BWC). Having this state-recognized self-insured program account in place allowed the hospital to include, with relative ease, the worker's compensation program coverage component in the Owner's project-specific insurance program. A separate sub-account was set up with the BWC to administer, monitor and manage project claims separately and distinctly from the hospital's self-insured account. Having all the project's workers enrolled in the Owner's self-insured program allowed all of the project team participants to remove the traditional worker's compensation premium charge from their bid pricing.

By requiring all major trade partners to participate in the project-specific insurance program, the BWC required that the premium rate normally charged to a project as part of the workers' hourly rate or overhead be scrubbed out of those hourly rates. The rates were Reimbursable Costs under the IALPD and verified by the Hospital's independent auditor.

In our case, the savings to be realized by beating the claims game and avoiding injury claims or unrecoverable premium payments went to fund the IPD Team's Incentive Compensation Plan. Allocating unspent insurance premium dollars to the Incentive Compensation Plan promotes safety in the work place and reinforces the message that safety awareness is everyone's concern.

Further, because the IPD Team agreed that all self-insured retention (deductible) payments which would be required as a result of a claim being filed would come from the fixed contingency fund established as part of the Target Cost, there was an additional incentive to avoid incidents that would result in a claim and deductible.

Tie Safety To Success — Safely

When it comes to incentivizing workplace safety, it's important to structure the safety program so that it doesn't incentivize workers to not file legitimate claims for fear of impacting the incentive plan for everyone else. As noted Part 1: Contract Basics in the Appendix, we included workplace safety as a Measure of Success. We used an industry measure known as a "DART" score (Days Away Restricted Transfer).

Safety was a discussion topic every day prior to starting work for that day. It was reinforced with group safety discussions, morning stretching exercises and weekly and monthly recaps of incidents and near misses experienced for the prior reporting period. The general contractor also had a program in place to assess incidents and near misses and implement changes in the way the work is done to avoid similar incidents in the future.

We also considered relying on an existing captive insurance program. The hospital insures its general liability exposure and professional liability exposure through this policy. We looked at the possibility of insuring all or some layer of the general liability and professional liability primary and excess coverage.

After analysis by our insurance team, we rejected the idea largely because the potential savings wouldn't be worth the trouble of setting up the coverage. The true benefit would have been at the primary insurance level, and the hospital wasn't comfortable taking on the primary layer of project risk under the captive policy.

The role that the captive insurance company might play could not be determined until after we got the underwriter on board to establish the range of the premium pricing for the types and layers of insurance. Did I mention, getting the underwriter on board was no easy task?

III. Choosing An Underwriter

The IPD Team selected the insurance underwriter in the same way it selected Oswald. In both cases, the Owner intended the underwriter to be part of the IPD Team.

We identified firms that had some working knowledge and experience with IPD, then defined a short list based upon interest in joining the IPD Team. Finally, the IPD Team identified and interviewed the candidates. Three firms expressed an interest in working with us to develop an insurance program that would support our IALPD as it addressed risk and rewards for the IPD Team.

We selected XL Insurance for a number of reasons:

- The XL team members were truly excited about being a part of the team and were innovative in thinking how to make their product work in our contractual framework.

- XL could provide all the lines of coverage we felt we needed in an integrated way that was virtually seamless to the IPD Team and Project. This was important because we did not want any gaps in the coverage, and we wanted to work with one company regardless of the nature of the claim. Just as we had a no-finger-pointing policy with the IPD team, we required a no finger-pointing approach to insuring the project risk. XL bought into insuring all the risk we asked it to cover.

- The XL Team crafted a policy that was consistent with our IALPD. For example, the IALPD contains a Waiver of Liability that states in part:

"Subject to the allowed Claims set forth in Section 12-2, the Parties, Cost Reimbursable Subcontractors and Cost Reimbursable Consultants (the "ICL Participants") waive and release all claims and liability between and among each other related to the performance of this Agreement or the Work that exceed the amount actually paid under any insurance policy required to be carried under this Agreement (or any applicable subcontract or consulting agreement)."

This sentence required a great deal of conversation among the insurance team members before the final policies were issued.

Administering Owner-Controlled Insurance

Oswald retained the services of Construction Insurance Partners (CIP) to help administer the Owner-controlled insurance program. This support included the preparation of the Owner Controlled Insurance Program Manual that was incorporated into the IALPD as an Exhibit. The purpose of the manual was to:

- replace the insurance requirements generally found and included in a traditional construction agreement with the general contractor;

- summarize the insurance coverage types to be provided under the Owner-controlled insurance program, including those additional coverage types not normally found in an Owner-controlled insurance program;

- outline any insurance coverage types that each subcontractor or consultant must provide on its own outside of the Owner-controlled insurance program;

- describe the enrollment and claims-filing procedures; and,

- summarize the project's mobilization program for bringing workers onto the site and administering safety requirements to all participants on the site.

Participation in and compliance with the insurance program was made mandatory for all contractors, subcontractors, architects, engineers and sub-consultants unless specifically excluded by the Owner in writing.

Enrollment was not automatic. As part of the mobilization program, workers needed to complete the enrollment paperwork with CIP and participate in a mandatory safety-training class. As the project ramped up during the construction phase, anticipating and monitoring the additional subcontractors and workers took a great deal of coordination among the onsite CIP claims administrator, the Welty/Boldt safety administrator and the Welty/Boldt supervisory staff.

Having a partner to manage the insurance program for the IPD Team is a must do. The CIP staff members are experienced in implementing these programs and proved to be an asset in helping contractors not familiar with this type of program understand how it applies to them.

The staff also took the lead in enrolling each member, requiring a nominal amount of information from the subcontractor to get the enrollment completed in a timely manner so as not to prevent the subcontractor from being on site when scheduled to start its work.

Maximizing The Value of The Claims Administrator

Our insurance program provided for a claims administrator to be retained and be on the site throughout the scheduled construction period. If your insurance program provides the same, be involved in the selection of this person because he/she will be part of the project's safety team. The administrator is responsible for investigating all incidents that result in an insurance claim having to be filed under either the general liability policy for third-party claims for damage or injury, builder's risk claims for property damage to the project, or injury to workers on the project site under the worker's compensation program.

The claims administrator is empowered to investigate every claim, compile the facts associated with the incident, and work directly with the insurance company's claims representative; or in the case of a worker's compensation claim, the hospital's medical claims administrator, in order to bring the incident to a final resolution.

An experienced claims administrator demands and deserves a respectable wage, so it's important for the IPD Team to reach agreement on how this individual's talents will be used by the IPD Team's safety program. Since the IPD method strives to eliminate the duplication of efforts and costs, this person should be considered a member of the safety team and be incorporated into the Safety Program adopted for the project. The claims administrator should serve as another set of "safety" eyes and ears on the project to ensure compliance by all workers.

We discovered however, some may interpret this position as being the "eyes and ears" of the Owner on the project. To address this, be sure to educate all participants on the claims administrator's role and responsibilities and stress that he/she is an integral part of the safety team.

Additional Insurances Required

Although the Owner-specific insurance program was structured to provide a broad range of coverage lines, those parties enrolled in the program were required to provide the following insurance at their own expense:

- Comprehensive Business/Automobile Liability Insurance to cover the use of the enrolled party's owned and hired automobiles whether on or off the Project site.

- Workers Compensation Insurance to cover worker's injuries and accidents in connection with the enrolled party's operations away from the Project site.

- Commercial General Liability Insurance in connection with the enrolled party's operations away from the project site.

- Equipment Insurance to cover loss or damage to the enrolled party's equipment, tools or other property.

Certificates of Insurance evidencing such lines of coverage and naming the hospital, Welty/Boldt and all enrolled parties as additional insured were required to be provided to CIP before an enrolled party was permitted on the site.

The CIP administration team also was responsible for collecting the payroll records from each enrolled party and reporting that information to the state Bureau of Worker's Compensation. The administrator also has audit rights to ensure the accuracy of the information being provided.

In order to simplify the administration of the program and not cause undue paperwork or hardship on the minor third-party contributors, the insurance team elected to exclude vendors, suppliers, fabricators, material-dealers, truckers, haulers, drivers and others that merely transport, pick up, deliver or carry materials, personnel, parts or equipment or any other items or person to or from the project site. This was expanded further after the construction activity started to exclude vendors or subcontractors that were going to be on the site sporadically and would not be incurring sufficient man hours to warrant tracking those hours in the worker's compensation program.

Table 1 is an example of the types of coverage considered for the Project along with the limits of liability for each type of coverage, and the applicable self-insured retention amounts. Also shown is how the limits were layered to take advantage of the price points in the marketplace while building the limits as determined by the IPD Team.

Owner's Project Coverage

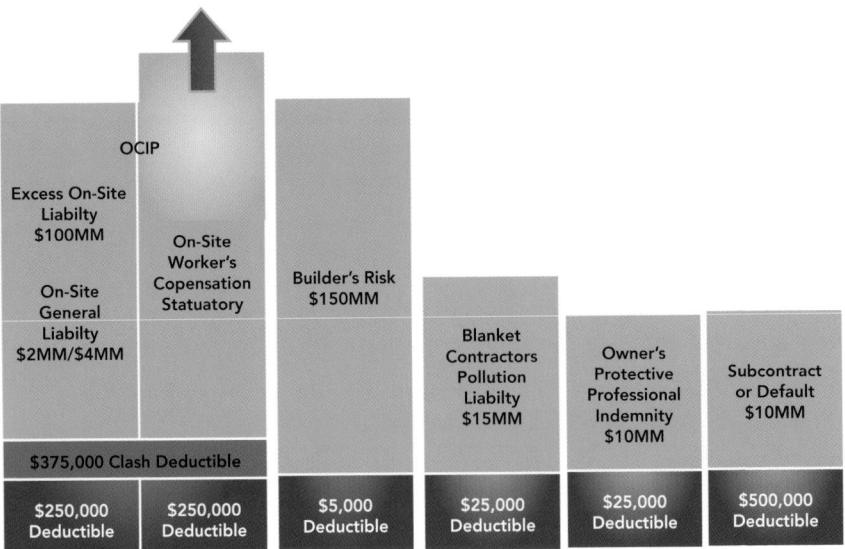

Conclusion

In retrospect, putting an Owner-controlled, project-specific insurance program in place takes a great deal of consideration and collaboration by an insurance team selected to make it happen. When you weigh the pros and cons associated with following the traditional project insurance methods and products versus a more integrated project-specific insurance program designed to support the IPD paradigm, the new project-specific insurance program makes a lot of sense.

As the underwriters of these insurance products become more familiar with the IPD method, and the number of IPD projects increase with few or no claims arising from these types of projects and insurance products, the ability to put this type of program in place will become easier.

A concern raised by every underwriter is what the courts will do when one of these IPD projects results in litigation between some of the parties. Since the Tower project's insurance program is a relatively new product in the insurance marketplace, we can only speculate what the answers might be. In our case, we tried to structure the IALPD to avoid such a scenario, and XL agreed to join us in the risks we took for project success.

V. Lessons Learned

- Select an insurance broker early in the process with knowledge and expertise in structuring an insurance program that is appropriate for your project.

- Determine early in project development how project insurance will be addressed: traditional insurance method; project specific insurance method either as an OCIP or CCIP; or some variation of the two.

- Make premiums and self-insured retentions/deductibles a project cost so everyone shares the risk.

- Determine who is responsible for self-insured retentions/deductibles under the different lines of coverage.

- Select an underwriter that can provide all coverage types for the project.

- Work with the underwriter and broker to make sure the policy language supports the integrated project delivery agreement.

- If you use an OCIP model, make sure the OCIP claims administrator is an integral member of the safety team.

PART 4: DOCUMENTS AND GRAPHICS

I. NICU, Outpatient Surgery and Emergency Department Teams

The NICU team

Outpatient Surgery team

Emergency Dept. team

II. Master Project Dashboard

Master Project Dashboard

1) Project Schedule

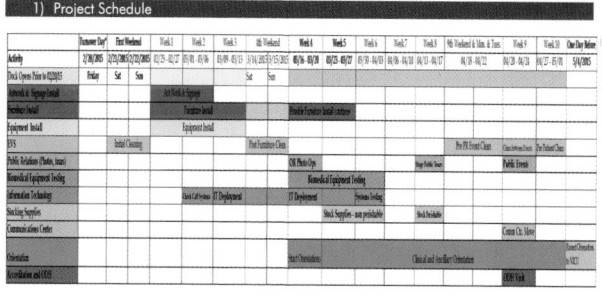

Akron Children's Hospital – Akron, OH
Critical Care Tower
Project Dashboard
September 18, 2014

3) Cashflow Update

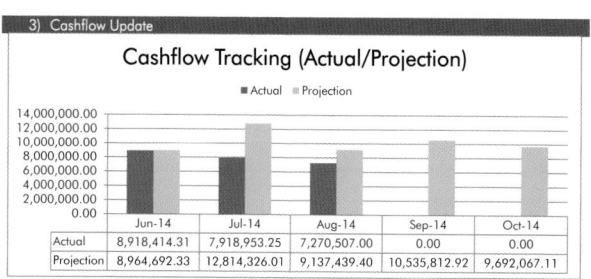

Cashflow Tracking (Actual/Projection)

■ Actual ■ Projection

	Jun-14	Jul-14	Aug-14	Sep-14	Oct-14
Actual	8,918,414.31	7,918,953.25	7,270,507.00	0.00	0.00
Projection	8,964,692.33	12,814,326.01	9,137,439.40	10,535,812.92	9,692,067.11

5) Upcoming Decisions & Issue Management

- Transition Update
- Success Metric Tracking – Currently Tracking 92/100

2) Project Schedule & Milestones

Project Meeting and Team Milestones – 6 Week look ahead
- 9/15/14 – Update on Perkins Square?
- 9/18/14 – SOC Meeting – Walk
- 9/22-9/26 – Team Week
- 9/23/14 – SET Meeting
- 9/25/14 – Board Member Site Walk
- 9/26/14 – Level 1 – Area 3 – Train Complete
- 10/13/14 – Weather Tight
- 11/28/14 – Atrium Lobby View of Park Avail.

Project Schedule Major Milestones

	CCT Tower Schedule Activity	Duration	Start	Finish
1)	Foundations	13 Weeks	6/24/13	9/20/13
2)	Super Structure	33 Weeks	8/12/13	3/28/14
3)	Mechanical/Electrical Rooms & Vertical Risers	26 Weeks	11/18/13	5/16/14
4)	Enclosure Backup & Roof	28 Weeks	11/25/13	6/6/14
5)	Main Distribution Overhead	30 Weeks	12/2/13	6/27/14
6)	Framing & Rough-Ins	28 Weeks	2/10/14	8/22/14
7)	Enclosure Finishes	33 Weeks	3/10/14	10/24/14
8)	Finishes	50 Weeks	3/10/14	2/20/15
9)	Landscaping	16 Weeks	8/4/14	11/21/14

4) Target Cost Update

ASST Project Totals - August 21, 2014

	Original Bond Values	Total Project Values
	$ 221,939,000	$ 226,544,091

Critical Care Tower

	Budget Values	Target Value	Commitments To Date	Actuals to Date	Delta (Commited/Target Value)
ASST 1640 - CBRE	$ 2,135,000	$ 2,135,000	$ 2,135,000	$ 1,401,279	$ -
ASST 1645 - Building	$ 153,664,611	$ 155,889,867	$ 155,889,867	$ 103,963,869	$ -
ASST 1651 - FF&E	$ 24,200,389	$ 24,200,389	$ 24,200,389	$ 155,152	$ -
ASST - 1645 - HROB Risk	$ 4,605,091	$	$	$	$ -
Subtotal - TOWER COSTS	$ 184,605,091	$ 182,225,256	$ 182,225,256	$ 105,520,300	$ -

Parking Garage

| ASST 1641 - Parking Garage | $ 20,000,000 | $ 19,150,000 | $ 19,039,057 | $ 18,944,228 | $ 110,943 |

Land Acquisitions & Utility Work

| ASST 1646 - Land Acquisition | $ 6,768,000 | $ 6,768,000 | $ 6,773,349 | $ 6,772,362 | $ (5,349) |
| ASST 1647 - Utility Work | $ 3,311,000 | $ 3,311,000 | $ 2,411,723 | $ 2,411,723 | $ 899,277 |

Interest & Bonds

ASST 1648 - Bond Issuance	$ 2,035,000	$ 2,035,000	$ 2,035,000	$ 1,300,000	$ -
ASST 1649 - Garage Interest	$ 1,245,000	$ 1,245,000	$ 1,245,000	$ 1,115,986	$ -
ASST 1650 - Tower Interest	$ 8,580,000	$ 8,580,000	$ 5,024,296	$ 5,024,296	$ -

| ASST Project Totals | $ 226,544,091 | $ 223,314,256 | $ 222,309,386 | $ 141,088,895 | $ 1,004,870 |

Changes from Budget Values to Target Values

CCT Original Bond Value	$ 180,000,000.00
Change for Shell Space - Lvl 4 & 5	$ (8,082,242.88)
Target Cost Adjustment A	$ 2,274,770.05
Target Cost Adjustment B Reduction	$ (1,287,436.11)
Target Cost Adjustment C - HROB	$ 11,700,000.00
Owner's Potential Risk - Maintain $180M Target	$ 4,605,091.06

Changes from Original Contingency

CCT Original Contingency Amount	$ 12,200,000.00
Target Cost Adjustment A	$ (2,700,870.00)
Target Cost Adj. B - ICL Profit (40% of Potential Profit	$ (5,176,021.78)
Target Cost Adj. B - Owner Profit Payment ($1M)	$ (1,000,000.00)
Target Cost Adjustment C - HROB	$ 300,000.00
Target Cost Adjustment - OH&P Reconciliation	$ (76,858.00)
Target Cost Adjustment D	$ (648,776.00)
Current CCT Contingency - ASST 1645	$ 2,597,474.22

Akron Children's Hospital

Ambulatory Care Center and Critical Care Tower

A3 #	Title
P100	Prefab NICU Bathroom Construction Method
	Discipline
	Production Team
	Participants: Production Innovation Team

OBJECTIVE (Relevance to ACH Project Wide Factors)

Identify a typical bathroom design/construction method to produce them with increased efficiency, safety, consistency and decreased project schedule. Bathrooms typically require multiple phases of construction, testing, inspection punch list and commissioning in order to coordinate multiple finishes, accessories and fixtures. The overlap of these phases can be greatly reduced by kitting or prefabrication because the unit(s) can be made and delivered by a single manufacturer in a controlled environment. Of the typical 69 NICU bathrooms there are approximately 62 that are identical or nearly identical. Minor varitions in the remaining configurations would be included in the alterate methods being considered.

RESEARCH (Options & Investigation Process)

The NICU bathroom construction method comparison includes 3 alternatives: Alt 1 - Site Fabricated (Standard expectations of site construction including individual trade prefabrication of certain scopes), Alt 2 - Site Modularized (Trade team would prefab roughed-in modular units on-site then move and set in final position. Finishes completed in place), and Alt 3 - Purchased (Vendor provides an almost fully prefabricated unit with finishes). Two bathrooms in a back to back arrangement were studied to capture the total cost of work including the demising wall and vertical plumbing stacks needed to complete/support the various bathroom construction methods. A CBA, a Cost/scope analysis, and a preliminary schedule/takt plan of the alternatives and potential general condition savings due to early completion were the research/investigation tools and processes used.

ALT 1 - SITE FABRICATED   ALT 2 - SITE MODULARIZED   ALT 3 - PURCHASED

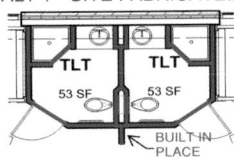
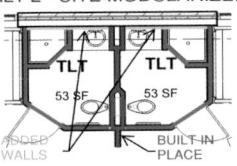

PROPOSAL (Recommendation)

The production team recommends the Alt 3 - Purchased method of construction for the NICU bathrooms due to the estimated schedule and costs savings. While the 3 week savings estimated around the driving activities of framing and drywall only is well within reason, it stands to err on the side of being conservative and establish a range of potential savings at 2-3 weeks ($150,000 - $225,000). We should proceed with a parameter of $75k savings/week and a requirement that schedule savings and associated GC savings must offset any premium costs associated with prefabrication as we consider final differences between Alt 3 - purchased approaches. Two companies (BLOX & Eggrock) were considered and provided input for Alternative 3 - Purchased. BLOX costs were lower by a significant margin and thus carried in the comparison. There are potentially significant differences in how to execute the Alt 3 - Purchased method. The critical difference is how each would treat the dimising wall and vertical plumbing stacks. BLOX proposes to carry a portion of the demising wall and veritcal plumbing stacks as part of a prefabbed unit with site connections and wall construction completion made above the pod set in place. Eggrock proposes to have prefabbed units placed against site built demising wall and vertical plumbing stacks. **The production team recommends proceeding by studying the differences and advantages of the two approaches, verifying committed final pricing and submitting an A3 and CBA for final recommendation of a provider and proposed approach.**

Date Opened		Date to be Closed (LRM)	Status	
02/05/13		04/22/13	■ In-Progress ☐ Closed / Approved	
Champion		**Decision Maker**	**Author**	
Rob Walter		Production Team	Rob Walter	

ANALYSIS (CBA summary or other analysis)

CBA - The top three factors/advantages on the CBA scale of importance are: (1) Cost & Schedule Predictability - Risks/Most predictable cost and schedule, (2) Construction Schedule/Most flexibility & opportunity to improve schedule, (3) Floor build out accessability/Most space available to access & complete construction work. The production team completed the construction method CBA with Alt 3 - Purchased at 375 points, Alt 2 -Site Modularized at 297 points and Alt1 - Site Fabricated at 51 points.

CBA Chart: Total Importance of Advantages at Price Points

COST - The Cost/Scope analysis established an estimated total construction cost for each alternative (not including general conditions). Construction costs were estimated for two back to back bathrooms including demising wall and vertical plumbing stacks. Considering 34.5 instances of back to back bathrooms the total cost differential/premium (before General Conditions): Alt 1 - Site Fabricated = $0, Alt 2 - Site Modularized = $147,567 and Alt 3 - Purchased = $115,884.

SCHEDULE & GENERAL CONDITIONS SAVINGS - The framing & drywall trade was determined to have the greatest impact to schedule due to the amount/nature of work. A takt time of 5 days was the basis for schedule analysis. When the bathroom framing & drywall activities for the bathrooms are removed and crew size is held constant, the analysis showed the elimination of one takt cycle (1 week) in each of the three areas (L6 North, L7 North & L7South) for a total saving of 3 weeks. General conditions costs for Welty/Boldt and the major trades amount to $75,000/week. Total potential savings = $225,000. Total project costs: Alt 1 - Site Fabricated = $1,296,338, Alt 2 - Site Modularized = $1,368,905 and Alt 3 - Purchased = $1,262,223.

PATH FORWARD (Action Plan)

What?	Who?	When?
Revisit CBA-Prefab Bathroom Partner Selection	Prod. Team	19-Mar
Detailed de-scope and analysis of diff. approaches	Prod. Team	27-Mar
Review commited final prcing from vendors	Prod. Team	1-Apr
Complete CBA-Prefab Bathroom Partner Selection	Prod. Team	1-Apr

REFLECTION (Any learnings?)

PROJECT WIDE FACTORS

Seven Flows of Healthcare	
	Patient Flow
	Family Flow
	Staff Flow
	Medications Flow
	Supplies Flow
	Equipment Flow
	Information Flow
Safety	
	Patient Safety
	Staff Safety
	Construction Safety
Cost	
	First Cost
	Life Cycle Cost
Schedule	
	Design
	Procurement
	Fabrication
	Installation
Impacts on Occupants	
	Patient Impact
	Family Impact
	Staff Impact
Future	
	Flexibility (surge)
	Expandability (grow)
	Adaptability (change)
Community Impact	
	Traffic
	Aesthetics
Evidence-base Healing	
Environment	
	Natural Light
	Landscape Integration
	Horticulture
	Acoustics
	Infection Control
Sustainability	
Quality	

Approval Signatures (if needed):

Children's
Hospital

Ambulatory Care Center and Critical Care Tower

IV. A3: NICU Headwall Study

NICU Headwall Study

A3 #	Title
P103.2	Medical Gas Head Wall Study - NICU
	Discipline
	MEPF, Interiors and Production Teams
	Participants: Production Innovation Team

OBJECTIVE (Relevance to ACH Project Wide Factors)

To determine how the medical gas head walls will be furnished and installed for the ACH project.

RESEARCH (Options & Investigation Process)

Current State of Estimate:
1. NICU - (75) modular head walls by Mitchell, hook-ups by Trade Partners
2. PACU - (14) modular head walls by Mitchell, hook-ups by Trade Partners
3. Pre-Op - (12) modular head walls by Mitchell, hook-ups by Trade Partners

Alternates Under Consideration:
1. Modular Head Walls by Mitchel, Hook-ups by Trade Partners
2. Prefab Head Walls by Trade Partners

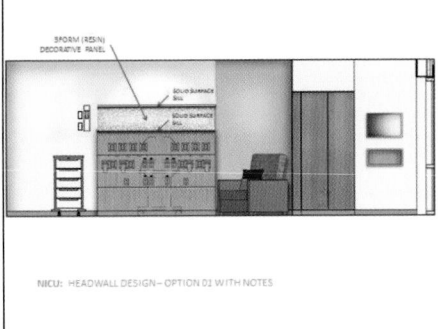

NICU: HEADWALL DESIGN – OPTION 01 WITH NOTES

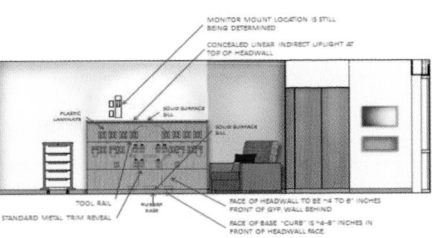

NICU: HEADWALL DESIGN – OPTION 02 WITH NOTES

PROPOSAL (Recommendation)

Team recommends the following: NICU Purchased
Headwall Option, pricing by Mitchell for Decorative Panel option (LH photo above)   ASC - Purchased Mitchell Headwall
options, pricing by Mitchell   **Mitchell pricing was updated on 04.10.13 and
does result in a savings to the project and also resulted in the purchased option being more cost effective for the project.**
We recommend the project purchase Headwalls through Mitchell and reduce the project cost to reflect the most current pricing
from Mitchell.

Date Opened	Date to be Closed (LRM)	Status	
01/09/13	06/28/13	☐	In-Progress
Champion	**Decision Maker**	**Author**	
Nick Loughrin/Pamela Best	PLT	Nick	

ANALYSIS (CBA summary or other analysis)

WELTY BUILDING COMPANY LLC

Purchased Headwall Units Compared to Trade Partner Outlets in Sheetrock (prefabbed)

Children's Hospital
March 17, 2013

PROGRAM COST SUMMARY

Description	Quantity	Unit	Unit Price	Subtotal	Total	Notes and Comments
ASC Purchased Headwall Units - OPTION #1						
Purchased Medical Equipment Headwalls				$ -		Mitchell
PACU	14	ea	$ 4,693.00	$ 65,702.00		
Pre-Op	12	ea	$ 995.00	$ 11,940.00		
Labor to install (W/B)	28	ea	$ 500.00	$ 14,000.00		W/B
Plumbing - Medical Gas		ea	$	$		Outlets & piping w/purchased units
Electrical	28	ea	$ 436.00	$ 12,208.00		Outlets & wiring w/purchased units
					$ 103,850.00	
ASC Trade Partner built Rough-In - OPTION #2						
Trade Partners						Outlets in drywall (prefabbed)
Medical Equipment	28	ea	$ -	$ -		
W/B Finish			$ -	$ -		
W/B Finish			$ -	$ -		
W/B Finish			$ -	$ -		
W/B Finish			$ -	$ -		
Medical Gas outlet & piping	28	ls	$ 2,239.00	$ 62,692.00		Outlets & piping Rough-In & Finish
Electrical outlets & wiring	252	ls	$ 145.00	$ 36,540.00		
KHS&S/ACP Headwall Rough-In	28	ls	$ 253.00	$ 7,084.00		
KHS&S/ACPHeadwall Finish	1	ls	$	$		
					$ 106,316.00	

WELTY BUILDING COMPANY LLC

Purchased Headwall Units compared to Trade Partner Prefab Finished Product

Children's Hospital
March 17, 2013

Cost Comparison

Description	Quantity	Unit	Unit Price	Subtotal	Total	Notes and Comments
NICU Purchased Headwall Units - OPTION #1						
Purchased Medical Equipment Headwalls (offset from	75	ea	$ 6,352.00	$ 476,400.00		Mitchell
Off-set from wall 4" with arkwork	75	ea	w/above	$ -		Mitchell
Labor to install (W/B)	75	ea	$ 480.00	$ 36,000.00		W/B
Plumbing - Medical Gas		ea	$	$		Outlets & wiring w/purchased units
Electrical	75	ea	$ 436.00	$ 32,700.00		Outlets & wiring w/purchased units
					$ 545,100.00	
NICU Trade Partner built Headwall Units - OPTION #2						
Trade Partners						
Medical Equipment	75	ea	$ -	$ -		Need Input from Mitchell
FC Dodson- Preconstructed w/No Topper	75	ea	$ 2,250.00	$ 168,750.00		
Labor to Unload Move and Install	75	ea	$ 1,320.00	$ 99,000.00		2 men - 12 hours
FC Dodson - Topper Pre-Attached (MAT)	75	ea	$ 500.00	$ 37,500.00		
Medical Gas outlet & piping	75	ea	$ 2,358.00	$ 176,850.00		Outlets & piping Rough-In & Finish
Electrical outlets & wiring	675	ea	$ 145.00	$ 97,875.00		
KHS&S/ACP Headwall Rough-In		None Included				
					$ 579,975.00	

PATH FORWARD (Action Plan)

What?	Who?	When?
See Production Last Planner		

REFLECTION (Any learnings?)

V. PLT Dashboard (partial view)

Akron Children's Hospital

Project Leadership Team
Management Dashboard

Week of September 22, 2014

PLT Goals

Description:	Due Date:	Decision:	Primary:
Exterior Trash Cans: Look alternate specification	23-Sep-14		John
ME223: Fire Alarm Existing Building Conduit Tie-In	23-Sep-14		Trent
Roller shade A3 transferring scope to W/B	23-Sep-14	Lin to verify need with hospital engineering team	Pat
		W/B to handle Roller Shades per Drawings and IN 302. Will be included in next DP.	
		Cubicle Curtains RFP to be sent by ACH.	
Review Design Projections	23-Sep-14	Need to get HROB projections included in this analysis	John
Receive Energy Model	23-Sep-14	Printed data can be provided; actual model will not be shared due to proprietary info;	John
		John to coordinate a call between Cliff and CORD likely to be Team Week	
Determine the complete scope of the "mouse hole"	23-Sep-14	Craig is preparing an A3	John
Playground Upgrades	23-Sep-14	Needs to be upgraded before blue mat is installed; need date for blue mat install	Pat
Review Sample Cubicle Curtain	23-Sep-14	Installed; being evaluated; install the suspended track for review	Marge
Review NICU Room Chair Storage Solution & Wall Covering Options	23-Sep-14	Being installed 7/29/14 - Need Room Numbers (Tim T or Paul)	Marge
Proposal from Osborn to Measurement & Verification 2 Points for LEED	23-Sep-14	Waiting to receive energy model	Cliff
Review Systems Furniture Bids	23-Sep-14		Stephen
Epoxy Flooring: Keep in Food Service, Food Washing, & Decon	26-Sep-14	Ardex cannot be used in SPD due to compatability with Epoxy flooring; need alternate flooring for SPD; W/B pulling together pricing for alternate	Trent
Recycling Compactor	26-Sep-14	HKS will research if anything was discussed during design meetings	Lin
Discuss Video in Trauma Booms	26-Sep-14	A3 is being created by user group	Marge
Patient Entertainment System	26-Sep-14	Waiting on information from Buchholz	Stephen
Review Responsibility Matrix	30-Sep-14	Need to review with W/B	Stephen
ET201: Getinge T-Doc Instrument Tracking	1-Oct-14	Need to decide on installation based on current LRM	Lin

LEED Added Value Items 35 agreed by USGBC points going into Construction. Tracking at 52 pts. Add to the Value

Success Metric Tracking & ICL Payment Scenario

	Total Points Possible
SAFETY	18
LOCAL PARTICIPATION	14
ENERGY EFFICIENCY	12
TEAM Performance	12
SCHEDULE	10
QUALITY	12
LEED	6
STAFF AND FAMILY SATISFACTION	16
Total	**100**

Incentive Layer Total	$5,413,066
Payment Based on 92% Score	$4,980,021
ICL Unallocated Funds (8%)	$433,045

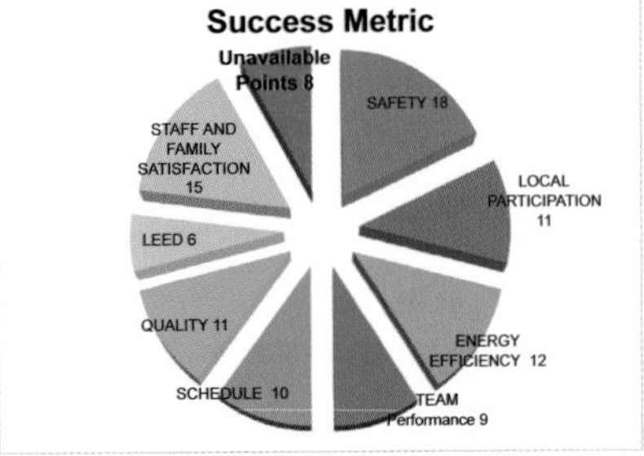

Success Metric

Unavailable Points 8
SAFETY 18
STAFF AND FAMILY SATISFACTION 15
LOCAL PARTICIPATION 11
LEED 6
ENERGY EFFICIENCY 12
QUALITY 11
SCHEDULE 10
TEAM Performance 9

Current Working Estimate - Cost Information

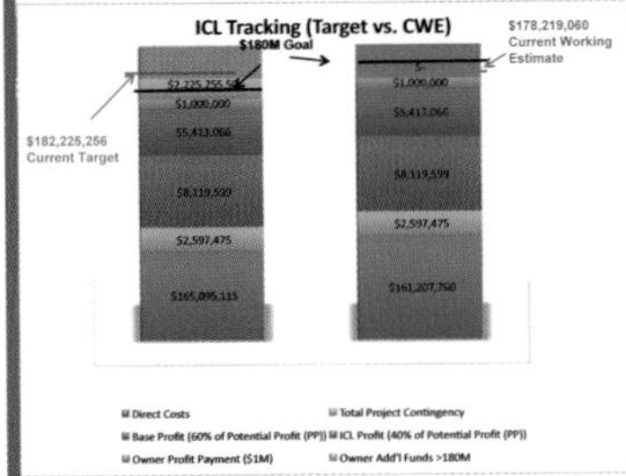

ICL Tracking (Target vs. CWE)

$180M Goal
$178,219,080 Current Working Estimate
$182,225,256 Current Target

$3,925,355,555
$1,000,000
$5,413,066
$8,119,599
$2,597,475
$165,895,115

$1,000,000
$5,413,066
$8,119,599
$2,597,475
$161,307,760

Direct Costs — Total Project Contingency
Base Profit (60% of Potential Profit (PP)) — ICL Profit (40% of Potential Profit (PP))
Owner Profit Payment ($1M) — Owner Add'l Funds >$180M

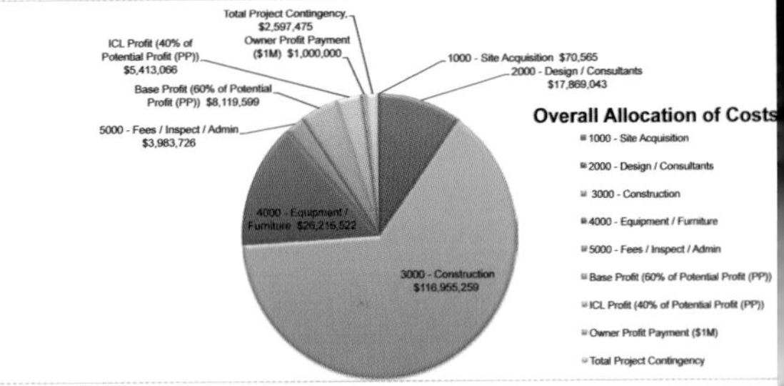

Overall Allocation of Costs

Total Project Contingency $2,597,475
Owner Profit Payment ($1M) $1,000,000
ICL Profit (40% of Potential Profit (PP)) $5,413,066
Base Profit (60% of Potential Profit (PP)) $8,119,599
5000 - Fees / Inspect / Admin $3,983,726
1000 - Site Acquisition $70,565
2000 - Design / Consultants $17,869,043
4000 - Equipment / Furniture $26,216,522
3000 - Construction $116,955,259

- 1000 - Site Acquisition
- 2000 - Design / Consultants
- 3000 - Construction
- 4000 - Equipment / Furniture
- 5000 - Fees / Inspect / Admin
- Base Profit (60% of Potential Profit (PP))
- ICL Profit (40% of Potential Profit (PP))
- Owner Profit Payment ($1M)
- Total Project Contingency

Contingency Usage Tracking

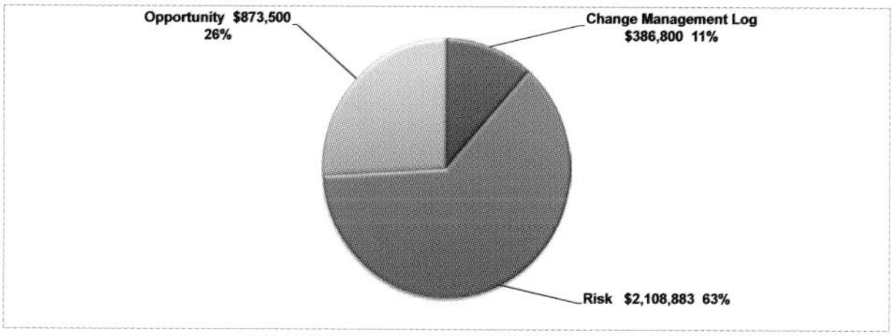

Opportunity $873,500
26%

Change Management Log
$386,800 11%

Risk $2,108,883 63%

As of August 22, 2014

Current Target	$	182,225,256	Through Target Adjustment D
Current Estimate	$	178,337,900	From Total Project Cost Tab - Based on 8/22/14 Projection
Delta	**$**	**3,887,355**	
Delta to Target	**$**	**3,887,355**	As of 8/22/14
Current Project Liability Allocation	$	3,887,355	
Current Cost Savings Under $180M	*$*	*1,662,100*	
Total Project Contingency	**$**	**2,597,475**	From Total Project Cost Tab - Based on Proposed Contingency

Potential Contingency Use

Change Management Log	$	(386,800)	Tab A- Current as of 8/18/14
Risk	$	(2,108,883)	Tab B - Based on WB 8/20/14
Opportunity	$	873,500	Tab B - Based on WB 8/20/14
Sub Total Contingency Remainder	**$**	**(1,622,183)**	Negative indicates Contingency Dollars Required
Total Contingency Amount Available	**$**	**975,292**	
Total Contingency plus Cost Savings Under $180M	*$*	*2,637,391.34*	

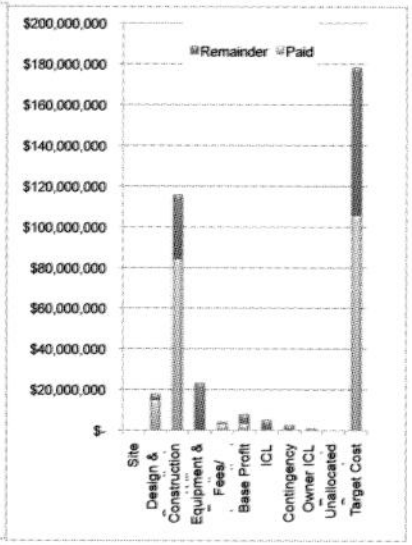

As of August 2014

		CWE		Paid to Date		Remainder
Site	$	63,565	$	63,241	$	324
Design & Consultants	$	17,928,755	$	14,942,530	$	2,986,225
Construction (All)	$	115,952,454	$	84,147,625	$	31,804,829
Equipment & Furniture	$	23,304,449	$	263,152	$	23,041,297
Fees/Inspection/Admin	$	3,958,536	$	2,918,641	$	1,039,895
Base Profit	$	8,119,599	$	3,185,111	$	4,934,489
ICL	$	5,413,066	$	-	$	5,413,066
Contingency	$	2,597,475	$	-	$	2,597,475
Owner ICL Payment	$	1,000,000	$	-	$	1,000,000
Unallocated Owner's Reserve		-	$	-	$	-
Target Cost	**$**	**178,337,900**	**$**	**105,520,300**	**$**	**72,817,600**

$200,000,000
$180,000,000
$160,000,000
$140,000,000
$120,000,000
$100,000,000
$80,000,000
$60,000,000
$40,000,000
$20,000,000
$-

Remainder Paid

Site, Design & Construction, Equipment &, Fees/, Base Profit, ICL, Contingency, Owner ICL, Unallocated, Target Cost

Postlude

Planning The Transition And Move

As the building construction continued in 2014, the work of preparing the clinical and support services for the move began with intensity.

As of fall of 2014, the gaps between the current state and the desired future state have been identified. Those gaps related to the physical space have been addressed during the design phase. Now it's time to zero in on work flows to bridge process gaps.

Equipment and furniture selections have been ongoing but will need to be finalized at this point. This may involve Furniture Fairs, team meetings, and conversations with the interior designers of the project. The original design team could lead this effort for the individual departments, being careful to document decisions and planning with the A3 documentation format. This will ensure the team will have "the plan in hand" when occupancy actually occurs and questions arise.

The transition planning also includes a pull plan of goals and associated activities for each department moving to or supporting the building. Each individual department pull plan will be entered into a spreadsheet to create the overall transition plan for the building. This tool will be used to monitor progress on a monthly and then weekly basis as the occupancy date draws near.

On a more global level the "fit up" planning for the actual structure is happening. The coordination of installations of the equipment and technology is critical to the overall success of the move and occupancy. "Last responsible moments" for installations are discussed, and coordination is planned so the furniture arrives before the computers are installed; and the wall mounts are installed before the monitors are due to arrive. All this activity must happen while the construction crews are completing the building.

At the point of turn over — when the occupancy permits have been obtained and keys are handed out — the departments will begin their orientation process, final equipment will be installed, and equipment and technology testing will occur.

Again, planning is key to coordinate all those activities even to the point of who will be in a particular space on a particular day.

We plan on sharing our work and our lessons learned in a second version Building a Lean Hospital, so stay tuned!

The Project Team, Akron Children's Hospital

Transitional Team — Pull Planning

Activity	Turnover Day*	First Weekend		Week 1	Week 2
	2/20/15	2/21/15	2/22/15	02/23 - 02/27	03/01 - 03/06
Dock Opens Prior to 02/20/15	Friday	Sat	Sun		
Artwork & Signage Install				Art Work & Signage	
Furniture Install					Furniture Install
Equipment Install					Equipment Install
EVS		Initial Cleaning			
Public Relations (Photos, tours)					
Biomedical Equipment Testing					
Information Technology					Check Call Systems
Stocking Supplies					
Communications Center					
Orientation					
Accreditation and ODH					

4th Weekend		Week 4	Week 5	Week 6	Week 7	Week 8	9th Weekend &
3/14/15	3/15/15	03/16 - 03/20	03/23 - 03/27	03/30 - 04/03	04/06 - 04/10	04/13 - 04/17	04/18
Sat	Sun						
		Possible Furniture Install continue					
Post Furniture Clean							Pre PR Ev
		OR Photo Ops				Stage Public Tours	
		Biomedical Equipment Testing					
		IT Deployment	Systems Testing				
			Stock Supplies - non perishable			Stock Perishable	
		Start Orientations		Clinical and Ancillary Orientation			

Transition/Occupancy Timeline

2014   **2015**   **Move Day May, 5th**

APR   MAY   JUN   JUL   AUG   SEP   OCT   NOV   DEC   JAN   FEB   MAR   APR   MAY

Construction Phase		In the Building
Department Teams doing process work and A3 Development	Pull Plan Development for each Department & Team Monitoring	Equipment Install Equipment Testing
Equipment Selection Ongoing	Master Pull Plan Developed and Monitored by Transition Team	Stocking

Planning
  - personnel
  - technology
  - supply needs
	Equipment Ordering and Staging	Orientation
		  - Scenario Testing
		  - Scavenger Hunt
		  - "Day in the Life"

	Final Furniture Selections and Order	Public Events/ Celebrations
	Pilots for Equipment/ Process Testing	

149